The NORTHERN PATH:

Norse Myths and Legends Retold . . . And What They Reveal

by

Douglas "Dag" Rossman

Published by Seven Paws Press

POB 2345, Chapel Hill NC 27515
Tel. 919.929.4287; Fax 919.929.7092
info@sevenpawspress.com
www.sevenpawspress.com

All of the stories in this collection have appeared previously, in a slightly different form, on the following audio-cassettes:

Ice & Fire: Tales from Norse Mythology (Skandisk, 1992)

Hammer & Mistletoe: Tales from Norse Mythology (Skandisk, 1993)

Troll Tales (Skandisk, 1994)

The Ring of Doom: The Saga of Sigurd (Skandisk, 1996)

ISBN 0-9649113-9-6
Library of Congress Catalog Card Number:
First Edition
First Printing, June 2005

Cover photo of Briksdal's Glacier in western Norway by Douglas Dag" Rossman. Author photo by Sharon Rossman. Cover design by Steven Forrest.

For information and orders of additional copies, please contact Seven Paws Press at the above address.

Dedication

In grateful memory of Snorri Sturluson (1179-1241),

Icelandic poet, historian, and storyteller. Without his Prose Edda,

many of the Norse myths would have been forever lost to later

generations.

And to all who would follow the Northern Path to Mimir's

Well, and there quench their thirst for wisdom and understanding,

this book is affectionately dedicated.

ACKNOWLEDGMENTS

I wish to thank Liv Dahl for giving me my first opportunity (in 1980) to tell the Norse myths at the Sons of Norway Fifth District Heritage Camp, Fall Creek, Wisconsin. That experience launched me on my avocational career as a Viking Age storyteller. I am grateful to the late Marion Nelson, former director of the Vesterheim Norwegian-American Museum (Decorah, Iowa), who began my long storytelling association with the Museum and with Decorah's annual Nordic Fest. His successor at the Vesterheim, Darrell Henning, not only continued to support my Nordic Fest appearances, but he collaborated with my wife, Sharon, and me in creating and developing our visual presentation of the myths as a major museum exhibition, *Echoes of Odin: Norse Mythology in Scandinavia and America* (September 2000-January 2001).

My heartfelt thanks go to Mike and Else Sevig of Skandisk, Inc. (Bloomington, Minnesota), who helped give my retellings of the myths and legends greater permanence by releasing them on a series of audio cassettes in the 1990s. The stories that appear in this book are adapted from the scripts I wrote for those tapes. The Sevigs also granted permission to reprint Sharon's drawing of the Nine Worlds that had previously appeared in my book *The Nine Worlds: A Dictionary of Norse Mythology* (Skandisk, 2000).

I am indebted to the authors listed in the selected bibliography for the knowledge and insights they have shared with their readers (including me); where I have discussed their original ideas in the text, I have tried to credit the sources. My sincere apologies to any I may have omitted inadvertently. Quotations from the *Poetic Edda* that appear in this book are my adaptations from an array of translations, and are not identical with any one of them.

Finally, I cannot say how deeply I appreciate the inspiration, encouragement, and constructive criticism provided by Sharon Rossman, Jodie Forrest, Dean Andersson, April Snellgrove, Edward W. L. Smith, Casey Dinger, and Elyse and Wyatt Underhill, each of whom read all or portions of the manuscript. Any shortcomings that remain, however, are solely my responsibility.

TABLE OF CONTENTS

SECTION ONE: Voices from the Viking Age—The Tales Retold

Author's Note

Many authors have translated or retold the Eddic myths and legends of Viking-Age Scandinavia, but I believe the book you hold in your hands may well be the first one that was written by an oral teller of those tales. I have been telling these stories since 1980 to audiences of all ages, and in a variety of settings from woodland campfire rings to modern auditoriums. Most of these performances take place in the Upper Midwest—the heartland of Nordic America—but I have carried them as far afield as Texas, Louisiana, Alaska, and even Norway.

The plots you will read are essentially as they were presented traditionally, but I have "fleshed out" some of the details, dialogues, and motivations where I felt they would make the stories more accessible to contemporary audiences. In doing so, I tried to respect the integrity and spirit of the original tales; e. g., I have not portrayed Loki as a "good guy."

I suspect that having individual storytellers present slightly different versions on a common theme, with asides that made the story more relevant to each particular audience, has always been an aspect of the art of storytelling. Some of the direct translations that have survived are so abbreviated that the tales would have been over all too soon when told to a live audience—unless the storyteller used his own inventiveness to elaborate.

To the best of my knowledge, the only significant liberty I have taken with any of the stories was to identify Skirnir as a Light Elf in "The Courtship of Gerd." The Eddas don't tell us exactly what kind of being Skirnir was, but we do know that he was the god Frey's servant/companion. Since Frey was given Alfheim ("Elf Home") as a tooth gift—the Norse equivalent of a christening present—we can assume he became the principal deity of the Light Elves. Thus my characterization of Skirnir as an Elf does not seem unreasonable. The moral code that I ascribed to the Light Elves in that story was inferred from scattered references to Elvish traits in the *Eddas* and in other old Germanic literature.

Finally, since these tales come out of an oral tradition and are meant to be read aloud, I offer the following pronunciation guide to the proper names you will encounter. These sounds are approximations, and may not apply in all cases.

a = "a" as in "father"	ö = "oo" but with pursed lips
e = "a" as in "sane"	ei = "aye" or "eh" in different dialects
i, y = "ea" as in "seat"	ae = "a" as in "man"
o = "o" as in "cook"	j = "y" as in "year"
u = "oo" as in "boot"	kj, sj = "sh" as in "shoot"

Where "g" is the first letter, it is hard as in "great."

Where "h" precedes a consonant, the "h" is a breathy exhalation.

Douglas "Dag" Rossman
"Ormsgard"
Decorah, Iowa
November, 2004

FOREWORD: A Return to the Viking Age

The Viking Age of Scandinavia lasted less than three hundred years, from approximately 800-1100 A. D., but the image of the fierce sea-warriors and their dragon ships has left an indelible mark on the Western World . . . even if some of the details are inaccurate (the horned helmets, for instance, for which there is no historical or archaeological evidence). Still, the Vikings—and the farm families who bore and raised them—were a folk dedicated to the heroic ethic, practical realists who recognized that life is hard, and that the best thing a person can do is to live courageously and honorably, and to face death with a smile. This heroic ethic is best summed up in the *drengskapur*, which appears on page 231.

The stories that were told in Viking times, for the entertainment and enlightenment of both adults and children, were about the gods and heroes who exemplified this same world view. After all, in the end, even the Norse gods would perish before the onslaught of the forces of Chaos. So what other purpose could there be but to live and die honorably?

The tales were often told by wandering storytellers or poets called *skalds*, who traveled from lord's hall to farmstead, entertaining all who lodged there in exchange for room and board. Occasionally, if the host was wealthy, the *skald* received some coins or an arm-ring as well.

Let us return now a thousand years into the past. We enter a long, sod-covered log building with its central fire pit, and we take a seat on one of the benches that line the walls. After enjoying a savory supper of stew and fresh-baked bread, we push aside our wooden bowls, lean back, and focus our attention on the *skald* who stands near the fire pit, casting a flickering shadow on the wall. All voices hush—one voice, his, is about to begin . . . .

PART ONE: ICE AND FIRE

These nine tales tell of beginnings: for instance, how the Nine Worlds came into being; how Odin All-Father gained his great knowledge, wisdom, and eloquence; and how the gods acquired their magical weapons. These stories, in effect, introduce the characters and set the stage for the cosmic tragedy that will be played out later in this book.

The Creation

The Nine Worlds of the Norse mythic universe are created from the corpse of the first giant, Ymir. The first gods, Dwarves, and humans also appear.

In the beginning there was nothing—neither earth nor sea—only the great yawning void that the gods later called Ginnungagap.

Time passed, if time even existed then, and the first of the Nine Worlds came into being. South of Ginnungagap there appeared a land called Muspellheim, a place of fire—of volcanoes and molten lava—guarded by a soot-covered, swarthy-skinned Fire Giant named Surt. Surt it is who shall come forth at the end of time to destroy all the worlds with his flaming sword.

North of Ginnungagap there formed the second world, a misty realm of frost and ice called Niflheim. At the very center of Niflheim there is a huge, bubbling spring called Hvergelmir from which eleven icy rivers flow. It was Hvergelmir that was to serve as the Well of Creation.

The northern part of Ginnungagap slowly filled with ice from the rivers of Niflheim, while the southern part of the void became lighted up with sparks and embers from Muspellheim. Where the ice and fire met, the ice melted and began to drip into the very center of Ginnungagap. This meltwater took on the sleeping form of a great manlike creature. Thus was created Ymir, the first of the Frost Giants.

While Ymir slept, he began to sweat beneath his armpits, and—strange to say—from this sweat there grew a male giant and a female giant. Stranger still, Ymir's legs mated one with the other, and one of them gave birth to a son. It is from Ymir's offspring that the race of Frost Giants comes.

You might ask what sustained Ymir during his long sleep. The same meltwater that formed Ymir also produced a great cow, Audhumla; it was her milk that nourished him. The cow, in turn, licked the salty blocks of ice that filled the northern part of Ginnungagap. By the end of the first day of licking, a man's hair appeared, on the second day his head, and on the third day he stepped forth from the ice fully formed. This was Buri, who would become grandfather of the first Aesir gods.

Buri fathered a son called Bor, who married the giantess Bestla. The couple had three sons—Odin, Vili, and Ve—the first gods to be known as the Aesir. These young gods soon came to despise Ymir, whom they perceived as being evil, so they fell upon him as he slept and slew him. So much blood flowed from his body that all the Frost Giants were drowned—save for one couple that found some debris to keep them afloat. From them all of the Frost Giants are descended.

Odin and his brothers took Ymir's corpse and made from it our world—from his blood the sea, from his flesh the earth, from his bones the mountains, from his teeth the rocks and pebbles, and from his hair the grass and trees. From Ymir's skull, they made the domed vault of the sky, then placed a Dwarf under each of the four corners to hold it up. Where did the Dwarves come from? The Eddas tell us that they were created from maggots crawling in Ymir's corpse, although—if you ask them—the Dwarves will deny it.

The three young Aesir gods threw Ymir's brains skyward to form the clouds, which you can see to this day. Then they took the sparks and embers blown out of Muspellheim and put them into the sky to form the sun, the moon, and the stars. To establish the daily cycles of dark and light, the gods assigned the responsibility of driving the chariots of night and day across the sky to a woman (Nott) and her son (Dag); likewise, a goddess (Sol) drives the chariot of the sun, and her brother (Mani) the chariot of the moon.

To the surviving giants, the gods gave the lands along the coast (Utgard, the outer holding—later to be known as Jötunheim, or Giant Home), but to keep the giants from causing mischief in the interior, Odin and his brothers used Ymir's eyebrows to build a high barrier around this green and verdant place they called Midgard, or Middle Earth.

Walking along the sea shore one day, Odin, Vili, and Ve came upon two trees, an ash and an elm. From these trees, the gods created a man (Ask) and a woman (Embla). Odin breathed life into them, Vili gave them intelligence and movement, and Ve granted them speech, sight, and hearing. The brothers were so pleased with their creation that they gave Ask and Embla all of Midgard for themselves and their descendants, the human race.

Then, for themselves, the Aesir created the world of Asgard, which lies high above the world of men but is connected to it by a fiery rainbow bridge called Bifrost that allows the gods to visit Midgard whenever they wish. There are many great halls in Asgard, but none is more famous than Valhalla, where Odin entertains the spirits of those warriors who fall in battle. Close to Asgard lies Alfheim, the home of the Light Elves—those bright, mysterious beings who are friends and allies of the gods.

Finally, we come to the greatest wonder of all. The whole of creation—the entire Nine Worlds—is bound together by an ash tree so immense that its boughs stretch above the heavens and its roots extend not only into Asgard, but into Giant Home—and even into the great spring in frosty Niflheim. This marvelous tree is called Yggdrasil, and it is under constant attack—by dragons that gnaw at the root in Niflheim, by deer and a goat that nibble at its leaves and branches, and by rot that infects its bark.

In time, such threats should surely destroy the Tree and bring it crashing down—and all the Nine Worlds with it—were it not for the Norns, three mysterious women who live in Asgard near a spring called Urd's Well. Each day these Norns mix the healing spring water with white clay from its bank, then smear the white paste on the trunk of the Tree—all the while chanting the *ørlög*, the rules that govern the cosmic order. As long as the Norns are true to their task, the Tree will survive . . . and so will the Nine Worlds!

The Trials of Odin

Knowledge and wisdom can only be gained by great personal sacrifice, as the god Odin discovers on the World Tree and at Mimir's Well.

When the Nine Worlds were still quite new, Odin realized that he would need great knowledge—and even greater wisdom—if he were to rule them well. There were unimaginable cosmic powers he must be able to understand and control if he were to fend off the forces of Chaos.

Thus, Odin undertook a "vision quest" to seek the knowledge he needed. Naked and alone he hung on the World Tree, Yggdrasil—and there he remained for nine nights. As it says in the poem "Words of the High One," from the *Poetic Edda:*

> "Nine long nights I hung
> Upon that windswept Tree,
> Pierced by a spear and pledged to Odin—
> Sacrificed, myself to myself,
> Upon that Tree whose roots arise
> Whence even the wisest know not.
>
> None gave me drink, none gave me bread;
> Looking down, I saw the runes and,
> Seizing them with a cry,
> Fell down from the Tree."

Thus Odin came to know the runes, those mysterious and powerful symbols which embody all of the physical and spiritual forces that make up the fabric of the Nine Worlds. Yet knowledge without wisdom is dangerous, for the possession of great power without having an understanding of when it should—or, perhaps even more importantly, should not—be invoked, can lead to great harm.

Odin then set his feet toward Jötunheim and there, at the base of one of the mighty roots of the World Tree, he came upon the sparkling waters of the Well of Wisdom, guarded by the wise giant Mimir, his mother's brother. Those who drink from Mimir's Well, it is said, gain the gift of insight—but the attainment of wisdom always requires sacrifice. Hence, when Odin asked for a drink from the Well, wise Mimir granted permission—provided his nephew was prepared to sacrifice one of his eyes for the privilege!

Odin promptly reached into one of his eye sockets and wrenched out the eye, which he placed in Mimir's waiting palm. The giant calmly dropped the eye into the Well, then filled a drinking horn with the spring's water and handed it to his nephew. After Odin had drained the horn, he still possessed the knowledge of the runes, but now could also see the connectedness of all things, the motives of all beings, and the consequences of all actions. It was a very quiet and thoughtful Odin who wended his way back to Asgard.

War of the Gods

A breach of hospitality leads the two tribes of gods, the Aesir and the Vanir, into a devastating conflict.

Now, it seems that the Aesir were not the only group of gods. Away in the West there lived the Vanir, a tribe of fertility deities who dwelt in a rich land called Vanaheim.

One of the Vanir, a woman named Gullveig, decided to pay the Aesir an unexpected visit. At first the Aesir were courteous to her, as the rules of hospitality require, but Gullveig could talk of nothing but gold—getting gold, handling gold, dreaming about gold. Gullveig talked and talked until her gold lust threatened to upset the peace of Asgard, a peace Odin valued so much that he made a great mistake. He violated the rules of hospitality and ordered that Gullveig be killed.

But that was easier said than done. Three times the Aesir spitted Gullveig on a spear and roasted her—slowly—over a fire. Three times she emerged from the fire unharmed . . . and the last time she was transformed in appearance. The woman who stepped forth from that fire looked as if she might have flesh of living gold. Thereafter she was called Heid, the Gleaming One, and instead of lusting after gold she spent her time practicing evil magic. In fact, it seems likely that Heid was the very first witch . . . and the ancestress of all wicked witches who were to follow.

The Vanir were very upset about the Aesir's breach of hospitality—even if Gullveig had been a less-than-perfect guest. The long and the short of it is that the Vanir declared war on the Aesir. The ensuing struggle was intense, for it involved powerful magic as well as swords and spears, axes and arrows. Lightning bolts were thrown, mountains were cast down, and the walls of Asgard were totally destroyed. But after a time it became apparent that neither side was likely to win, so a truce was declared and hostages exchanged.

For their part, the Vanir sent Njörd, the god of ships and fishing, and his son, Frey, and daughter, Freyja, to live with the Aesir. The Aesir, in turn, sent the handsome god Hoenir and Odin's uncle, the wise giant Mimir, to the Vanir. All went well until the Vanir became suspicious of Hoenir's constantly referring all questions to Mimir. They began to think that Hoenir's handsome face concealed an empty head . . . and that the Aesir had not acted in good faith when they sent him as a hostage.

At that point, the story takes a strange twist, for, in order to make their displeasure plain to the Aesir, the Vanir cut off Mimir's head—not Hoenir's, as one might expect—and sent it back to Asgard. After his initial shock and anger, however, Odin decided it was wisest to ignore the insult. Not being one to waste a wise head—even if it were no longer attached to Mimir's shoulders—Odin magically preserved his uncle's head and restored its ability to speak. Thus Mimir continued to share his wisdom with his nephew Odin.

The Walls of Asgard

The walls of Asgard, destroyed in the war with the Vanir, must be rebuilt. But is the price too high? Loki, the Trickster, takes a hand.

With the walls of Asgard no longer standing, as a result of the war with the Vanir, the Aesir were understandably worried and ill at ease. What would keep the giants out if ever those big fellows decided to march into Asgard across the Rainbow Bridge?

Imagine then the gods' surprise when, one morning, there came a loud "Halloo" at the portal of Valhalla. When the Aesir went outside to see who called, they found a stone-mason sitting astride his horse with the tools of his trade strapped across its flanks.

"What can we do for you, stranger?" asked Odin. The man smiled back and drawled, "From what I've seen of your walls, I'd say it's more a matter of what we can do for each other. I'm a master builder, you see. You need new walls, and I need the work. It's as simple as that."

"Hmph," snorted Odin. "Things are rarely as simple as they seem. How long would it take you to complete the job?"

"Oh, I'd say your walls would be as good as new—maybe even better—in three seasons. After all, it is a lot of space to enclose."

"And your price?" queried Odin.

"Well-l-l now, I'm a modest man with modest needs. My home is a dark and lonely place right now, and what it really needs to brighten things up is a good wife and some better lighting. My price is the lovely Freyja . . . and the sun and the moon besides."

"Whaaat?" roared Odin. "You call those modest demands? It's altogether out of the question!"

But Loki, the mischievous young giant who lived in Asgard as Odin's blood-brother, hissed: "Wait a minute, wait a minute—let's not be hasty. Let's think about this fellow's offer a bit more." And Loki pulled Odin aside and whispered in his ear, "Don't throw away a chance to get the walls rebuilt. If my giant cousins should go on the warpath, we're going to need those walls."

"I am not going to sacrifice Freyja . . . let alone the sun and the moon," snapped Odin.

"You won't have to," replied Loki, "if you set conditions the mason can't possibly meet. If he tries and then fails, we'll at least get as much of the walls as he does put up—and it won't cost us anything."

"Count on you for the cunning idea, Loki," said Odin admiringly. Then the god turned to face the mason. "Very well, fellow, we'll agree to your price—but only if you agree to our terms. The job must be completed by the first day of summer—that will give you one season, not three—and you have to do all the work yourself, no helpers."

"That's nigh unto impossible," spluttered the mason. "Still, if there's even the slightest chance of winning the beautiful Freyja, it's worth the risk. Yes, I'll agree to your terms, but—er—would it be all right to use my stallion, Svadilfari, to help drag the stones from the quarry? After all, he's not a person, just a horse."

Odin frowned and hesitated, but seeing Loki eagerly nodding his head, Odin slapped hands with the mason to seal the bargain.

The mason began work that very afternoon. He set up camp in an abandoned quarry at the base of the hill below Valhalla, and immediately began to cut and dress blocks of stone to form the new wall around Asgard. With the help of Svadilfari, his great gray stallion, the mason easily dragged the blocks up the hill and set them into place.

The work proceeded rapidly—much too rapidly for the gods' comfort. Svadilfari might be just a horse, but surely he was no ordinary horse . . . and it was becoming abundantly clear that the mason was no ordinary man. Both man and horse were far too strong to be no more than what they appeared.

When only three nights remained until the deadline, Odin called Loki aside and said: "Loki, I don't know why I ever listen to you. Only the supports and arch for the gate remain to be built, and the mason can easily do that in a day or two. Asgard will become a dark and lonely place when he takes Freyja, the sun, and the moon away with him. You got us into this mess, Loki; can't you get us out of it?"

"Don't worry, Odin. I think I know just what to do," the Trickster assured the Allfather. "Just trust me."

"It seems I have no other choice," sighed Odin, for he could think of no honorable solution to their dilemma.

The next morning, just after the mason had hitched Svadilfari up to his first load, what should wander into the quarry but a beautiful young filly. She proceeded to turn her back coyly on the great stallion, flick her tail provocatively under his nose, and whicker enticingly as she moved away with mincing little steps.

Svadilfari was entranced, and all thoughts of his duty and loyalty to his master were replaced by this vision of equine delight. The filly began to prance away more rapidly and, with a loud, passionate whinny, Svadilfari snapped his traces and galloped after her. But as fast as he ran, the filly always managed to outdistance him, so it wasn't long before the two horses were almost out of sight.

The stunned mason shook himself out of a momentary daze, screamed "Hey, come back here!" at the top of his lungs, and charged after the horses as fast as his legs would carry him.

The horses were never seen again, but as the sun rose in the eastern sky on the first day of summer, the Aesir looking down from atop their new wall saw the figure of a man plodding wearily up the hill along the path from the old quarry. It was the stone mason, bleary-eyed and exhausted from three days of fruitlessly trying to catch his lost stallion.

When the mason reached the foot of the wall and observed the gods watching him and laughing at his discomfort, he shook his fist up at them and shouted: "'Tisn't fair, I tell you, 'tisn't fair. You cheated me. I would have finished that wall with time to spare if you hadn't sent that blasted filly to lure away my horse."

Odin looked down at the mason with folded arms, and calmly remarked: "And you wouldn't have been able to complete your work so swiftly without the help of a magic horse, so I think you have little to complain about, mason. The fact remains that you did not meet your deadline, so we thank you for as much of the wall as you did complete . . . and suggest that you be on your way."

"Cheat me, then turn me out like some beggar, would you? Well, I think not," declared the enraged mason, whose body was beginning to change shape and grow alarmingly large. "What I built, I can tear down," bellowed the shape-shifting giant as he gripped the top of the wall in both hands and began to brace his feet against its base.

Just then, as luck would have it, who should come striding up the hill but Thor, the Thunder God, home from a trip to the East where he had been hunting giants and trolls. Well, as soon as he saw the giant trying to pull down the wall of Asgard, Thor paid the mason his wages all right, though they weren't what he had bargained for.

Thor swung his mighty oaken club—in those early days he had not yet gotten his wonderful hammer—and shattered the giant's skull into a hundred pieces. And, should you ever visit Asgard, you'll still find fragments of that skull scattered along the hillside above the old quarry.

All the Aesir wondered what had happened to Loki, but some eleven months passed before the Trickster showed up one day at the now-completed gate of Asgard.

"It has been a strange year, Odin, the strangest that any man could experience. But I have brought you a special present." And Loki led forth a handsome gray colt, perfect in all ways—but, wonder of wonders, he had eight legs. "This is my son, Sleipnir, who will be a faithful companion on all your long journeys. He is absolutely tireless, and he can run over the sea and through the air as easily as on land."

Needless to say, Odin was delighted, and even those Aesir who disliked Loki because of his mischief-making had to admit that Sleipnir was a princely gift. Thus no one objected when Odin allowed Loki to marry the beautiful goddess Sigyn.

The Mead of Poetry

Brewed by two wicked Dwarves from the blood of the wise Kvasir, the Mead is acquired by the giant Suttung. Odin must recover it for the gods, using cunning rather than force.

When the Aesir and the Vanir ended their war and exchanged hostages, they all pledged their eternal friendship by spitting in a cauldron—thus mingling their life essences. And to give visible substance to this pledge, the Aesir mixed the spittle with clay and formed a man-like being, whom they called Kvasir.

Since Kvasir contained the essences of all the gods and goddesses, he was so wise that he could answer any question put to him. Kvasir wandered far and wide and, because he shared his vast knowledge freely with anyone who wished it, he was a welcome guest wherever he visited.

It came to pass, however, that two wicked Dwarves—Fjalar and Galar, by name—grew envious of Kvasir's wisdom and jealous of his popularity, so they decided to do something about it. On the pretext of needing him to solve a knotty problem for them, Fjalar and Galar invited Kvasir to visit them in their cave by the sea. The unsuspecting Kvasir (who though wise was innocent) came and, when they had him safely out of sight of prying eyes, the Dwarves fell upon Kvasir and stabbed him to death with their sharp little knives. Oh, how his blood flowed! Fjalar and Galar caught it as it came, and there was so much blood that it filled two cauldrons and a bucket.

After they had disposed of Kvasir's body, the Dwarves mixed his blood with honey to create a magic mead—and anyone who drank of it would thereby become a poet, for all know that poetry often contains great wisdom. After a time, the Aesir sent a messenger to inquire about Kvasir's whereabouts and well-being. Fjalar and Galar replied that because no one was sufficiently learned to be able to ask Kvasir enough difficult questions that he could let all of his knowledge emerge, Kvasir had simply choked to death on his own wisdom. Improbable as it seems, the gods apparently accepted this explanation—at least if any of them had suspicions, he kept them to himself.

Shortly thereafter, Fjalar and Galar—for reasons known only to them—invited the giant Gilling and his wife to come for a visit. The Dwarves offered to take Gilling for a boat ride, and when they had rowed far enough from shore to be over deep water, they deliberately capsized the boat. Gilling could not swim and he sank like a stone. Fjalar and Galar could only dog-paddle for a short distance themselves, but that was enough to let them splash back to their overturned craft and clamber up onto its keel. There they perched like a pair of seagulls while the boat slowly drifted back to the shore.

When the Dwarves told Gilling's wife what had happened to her husband—without, of course, revealing the cause of the so-called accident—she wept so hard and so long that the Dwarves' cave filled up with her tears and their furniture threatened to float away. Well, that would never do, so Fjalar whispered something in Galar's ear, and Galar slipped quietly out of the cave. Then Fjalar turned to the giantess and said: "Dear lady, do you think it might make your loss easier to bear if you could see the exact place where your poor husband sank beneath the waves?"

"Maybe so," she sobbed. So Fjalar led her to the cave mouth and pointed out to sea. When the giantess leaned forward to get a better look, Galar dropped a millstone on her head. And that was that, or so the two Dwarves thought.

Gilling's son Suttung caught wind of what had happened to his parents, and it wasn't long before he showed up on the Dwarves' doorstep. The tide was out—and turning a deaf ear to their denials and pleas—Suttung snatched up Fjalar in one hand and Galar in the other and waded out until he was chest deep, then dumped the wicked pair on a small rock exposed by the low tide.

"If you like the sea so much," he growled, "I'm sure you'll have great sport when the tide comes in."

Fjalar and Galar were terrified, for they knew they could never swim all the way to shore once the rock was covered. So they confessed all to Suttung, and begged him to accept compensation for his parents' deaths and to let the Dwarves live. Suttung muttered in his beard for a time, but he finally agreed to their proposal . . . and when he had deposited Fjalar and Galar at their cave and departed for Jötunheim, he carried the three vessels containing Kvasir's blood away with him.

When he got home, Suttung hid the magic mead in a cavern deep within the lonely mountain called Hnitbjörg. Then he made his daughter Gunnlöd stay in the cavern to guard the vessels.

Well, it's hard to keep such goings-on a secret for long, and word soon found its way to Asgard concerning what had happened . . . and the whereabouts of Kvasir's blood.

Odin decided to take matters into his own hands and, quicker than you could name the Nine Worlds, he was trekking through Jötunheim disguised as a one-eyed young giant named Bölverk. When he entered the lands belonging to Suttung's brother, Baugi, Odin came upon nine of Baugi's field hands cutting hay. The work seemed to be going slowly, so Odin offered to sharpen their sickles with his magic whetstone. This worked so well that each of the field hands wanted the whetstone for his very own. Odin agreed to sell the stone to the man who could catch it . . . and, saying this, he tossed the whetstone high into the air above their heads.

Well, with all of the pushing and shoving to be the one standing beneath the whetstone when it came down—and it seemed to be taking forever—the field hands managed to cut each other's throats with those razor-sharp sickles. So, when Odin stepped up to pluck the whetstone out of the air, not a single field hand remained alive. Odin smiled a grim smile and found a wooded thicket nearby where he could rest concealed until nightfall.

That evening Odin arrived at Baugi's hall and asked for supper and a night's lodging. These he was granted, but it was clear that his host was in a foul mood. When Odin asked what was the matter, Baugi replied: "My foolish field hands have gone and killed each other, that's what, right down to the very last man. Now how am I going to get my hay harvested? It will just rot in the fields."

"That is bad luck," responded Odin. "Still, your luck may be about to change for the better. You could hire me to take their places."

"You? One man to do the work of nine? What kind of fool do you take me for?" snapped Baugi angrily.

"I'm stronger than I look," replied Odin calmly. "Besides, what other choice do you have if you want to save your hay?"

"None, I guess," admitted Baugi. "Well, what would you expect as wages?"

"Oh, not much, really. I've always fancied I'd like to be a poet, so one drink of Suttung's mead would be wages enough for me."

"That mead is not mine to give," grumbled Baugi. "Ask for something else."

"No-o, it's the only thing in these parts I'm interested in. So if you want my help . . . ."

"All right, all right. If you do the work, I'll ask Suttung to give you a drink of his mead . . . but that's all I can promise."

Odin agreed to Baugi's offer and spent many days working from dawn to dusk cutting hay. When the job was done, he went to Baugi and demanded his wages. The giant hemmed and hawed but finally took Odin to see Suttung, and he asked his brother to fulfill Baugi's part of the bargain. Suttung just laughed in their faces, for he had had no part in making the bargain and felt no obligation to help out his brother.

Baugi was very unhappy that Suttung would shame him in this way, so when Odin asked his help in stealing some of the magic mead, Baugi was not slow to agree. That night they stole away to the back side of Hnitbjörg, where Odin handed Baugi a magic auger and asked him to bore a hole through the side of the mountain into the cavern where the vessels of mead lay hidden.

Baugi drilled and drilled, then stepped aside, saying that the job was done. Suspicious, Odin knelt down and blew into the hole. When stone chips flew back into his face, he knew that Baugi had played him false, and Odin demanded that the giant complete his task. So Baugi drilled again, and this time when Odin blew into the hole, nothing came back but the flow of cool air from the cavern.

At once, Odin took on the form of a serpent and crawled into the hole. Startled by the transformation, Baugi tried to stab Odin with the auger, but he just missed the serpent's tail as it wriggled out of sight. Fearing Suttung's anger should he discover his brother's role in the affair, Baugi decided to go home and say nothing.

When Odin entered the cavern, he resumed the form of the young giant, Bölverk. Now when Suttung's daughter, Gunnlöd, beheld the handsome stranger smiling at her, she forgot all about the fact that he shouldn't be there. It had been boring and lonely in that cavern ever since her father had made her stay there, and she craved companionship. So, when Odin started sweet-talking Gunnlöd, it wasn't long before she fell madly in love with him and offered not only her own sweet self, but anything else that was in her power to grant him. And Odin? Well, he accepted all that she offered . . . and on the third day of his visit, he asked Gunnlöd for one sip of mead from each of the three vessels.

The giantess didn't see how "just one sip" could possibly hurt her father, so she granted Odin's wish. Alas for the poor trusting girl! For with each sip, Odin swallowed the entire contents of each vessel. As soon as he had drained the last one—and without even saying "goodbye" to the stunned Gunnlöd—Odin changed into an eagle and flew out through the tunnel that Suttung used to visit the cavern.

Now it so happened that Suttung was on his way to Hnitbjörg, when the eagle that was Odin emerged from the mouth of the tunnel and soared skyward. The giant immediately sensed what had happened and, changing into an eagle himself, set off in hot pursuit. Ah, what a race it was! Odin had a head start, but all that mead he was carrying in his stomach slowed him down, so little by little Suttung gained on him. But, just as Suttung was about to catch him, Odin sailed over the walls of Asgard and spewed out the mead. It cascaded down into the cauldrons the Aesir had hastily set about in the courtyard when they saw the eagles coming from afar. Frustrated and furious as he was, Suttung had sense enough not to follow Odin into Asgard, and so he turned back toward his own land.

Odin let the Aesir drink of the magic mead . . . as he did those humans who showed some promise as poets. As for Gunnlöd—while the Eddas are silent on the matter—it seems likely that nine months later she might have given birth to a son who, when he grew to the proper age, would have been sent to Asgard to be raised by his father. And it also seems likely that Odin would have thought it only fitting that the boy should drink of the magic mead. What we do know is that Odin's son Bragi did so—more than once—and when Bragi was grown to manhood, he came to be known as the God of Poetry.

Gifts for the Gods

One of Loki's tricks goes wrong, but in trying to set things right he gains some wonderful gifts from the Dwarves—and puts his own head at risk!

Early one morning in Asgard, before the Chariot of the Sun had yet appeared over the eastern horizon, Thor the Thunder God was away from home, partying with Heimdall and some of his other friends.

Loki, the mischief maker, was wandering abroad, grumbling about not being invited to Heimdall's party, when he happened to pass by Thor's hall. Knowing that Thor was not at home, Loki peeked in the bedroom window and, sure enough, there lay Thor's beautiful wife, Sif, sound asleep. Now Sif's crowning glory was her long, silky blonde hair. It was the color of newly ripened grain, and she was rather vain about it. Loki couldn't stand vanity in anyone but himself—and, truth be told, he was a handsome fellow—so he saw a way to put Sif in her place and, at the same time, get back at Thor for going to the party without him.

Loki slipped through the window, stole quietly across the floor to the bed, pulled out his knife—and quickly, but thoroughly, cut off all of Sif's hair, leaving nothing but stubble. Pausing for a moment to admire his handiwork, Loki swiftly left the room the way he had entered it—through the window. Once outside, however, his curiosity overwhelmed his good sense and, instead of making himself scarce, he decided to hide below the window sill so he could hear all the fun when Sif discovered her loss.

And that wasn't long in coming. Sif awoke, yawned once or twice, stretched luxuriously, and sat up on the edge of her bed. As was her custom, she then picked up a hand-mirror to admire her gorgeous head of hair. She looked once, shook her head in disbelief, then looked again. Sif dropped the mirror, then slowly—oh, so slowly—raised her hands to her scalp. When her touch confirmed what the mirror had tried to tell her, Sif let out a wail. Sobbing as if her heart had broken, she pulled the sheet over her head so no one could see her disgrace. It was thus that Thor found her when he returned home a short time later.

"Darling, what's wrong? You're not mad 'cause I was out all night, are you? You know that Heimdall's parties always last until dawn."

"Boo-hoo."

"Aw, c'mon Sif. Tell me what's wrong. And why are you covered up with a sheet like that?"

"Boo-hoo. You wouldn't understand."

"Sure I would, sweetheart. Just try me."

"Well, all right," Sif said as she removed the sheet from her head.

"Aargh!" yelped Thor, taking an involuntary step back.

"See," sniffed Sif, yanking the sheet back over her head, "I knew you wouldn't understand."

At this point, Loki could restrain himself no longer, and the sound of his laughter reached Thor's ears. Letting out a snarl, the Thunder God strode to the window, reached down, grasped Loki by the neck, and dragged the Trickster, kicking and choking, into the room.

"S-o-o-o, Loki. I might have known you'd be at the bottom of this. What do you have to say for yourself?"

"I can't say anything with your hand crushing my throat," Loki gagged. "Put me down, put me down."

Thor dropped Loki in a heap on the floor. "Well, speak up."

"It was just a little joke," Loki whimpered. "Don't you people have a sense of humor?"

Thor glowered. "Do you see Sif laughing, Loki? And when Sif isn't amused, I'm not amused. And when I'm not amused, heads tend to get smashed. So you'd better do something about your 'little joke,' and you'd better do it quick."

Loki rubbed his neck gingerly and thought rapidly. "Oh, I know just what to do, Thor. And I'm sure you and Sif will be pleased with the results. Just trust me."

"Hmph. *That* will be the day." Thor raised a menacing fist. "Well, what are you waiting for? Begone!" And Loki went.

Where he went was to Svartalfheim, the underground world of the Dwarves, those magical master craftsmen. After passing through a maze of tunnels, Loki arrived at last at the cavern that served as the home of two Dwarves known as the Sons of Ivaldi. The Trickster explained his problem to them and, in exchange for the solemn promise of future favors, they set about forging a skein of hair made of living gold that could be attached to Sif's scalp. Then, while the forge was hot and they had more magic gold to spare, the Sons of Ivaldi decided they might as well make some other gifts to please Odin and Frey, as well as Thor. After all, one could never enjoy the favor of too many gods. So, the Dwarves made a small dragon-ship for Frey, and a rune-spear for Odin.

Loki was delighted with the outcome of his visit to the Sons of Ivaldi and, gathering up their gifts, he wended his way back toward the surface of the earth. But before he had gone very far, Loki came upon another Dwarf of his acquaintance, a proud little fellow named Brokk.

"Greetings, Brokk."

"Hello, Loki. What have you got there?"

"Oh, these are some gifts the Sons of Ivaldi have made for Odin, Frey, and Thor. Aren't they marvelously well crafted? Surely no other Dwarves could make anything nearly so fine."

"My brother, Eitri, could," snapped Brokk.

"Surely not. I'll bet he couldn't," teased Loki.

"And just what would you be willing to wager?" queried Brokk cunningly.

"Oh, I guess I'd bet my head," chuckled Loki carelessly, not taking Brokk very seriously.

"Done," said Brokk as he slapped Loki's hand to seal the wager.

Loki gulped, but he could not very well back out of the wager since he knew full well that if he did, Brokk would soon spread the story throughout the Nine Worlds, and Loki would become a laughing-stock—a fate he could not abide. For once, it seemed, the Trickster had been trapped by his own too-clever tongue.

Well, Brokk and Eitri set to work to create three gifts from their own store of magic gold, at least one of which they hoped would surpass anything made by the Sons of Ivaldi. Brokk operated the bellows to keep the temperature of the forge constant, and Eitri crafted the softened metal on his anvil. Loki excused himself from the cavern, saying that he had so much at stake he could not bear to watch.

But once out of sight, Loki transformed himself into a horsefly and, flying back into the cavern, he bit Brokk on the hand in hopes it would distract the Dwarf enough that he would stop pumping the bellows, thus letting the forge cool. Alas for Loki, Brokk was made of sterner stuff. He ignored the bite, and shortly thereafter his brother was able to hammer out a magnificent golden boar.

A second time the magic gold was placed in the forge. This time Loki—the horsefly—bit Brokk on the neck, but still to no avail. And the gift that Eitri produced was a beautiful arm-ring of massive size and intricate design.

It is said that "the third time pays all" and, when the last of the magic gold went into the forge, a desperate Loki landed on Brokk's eyelid and bit him so hard that blood ran down into the Dwarf's eye. Well, this was too much for even the stoic Brokk to ignore, and he used one hand to wipe away the blood. When he did so, of course, he had to stop pumping the bellows—and the forge began to cool before Eitri had time to draw out the last gift, a small hammer. It had a well-shaped head, but it was a little short in the handle because it couldn't be finished properly. The brothers had used up all of their gold, so they had to be content to send the hammer to Asgard as it was.

Loki and Brokk trekked back to Asgard to let the gods who would be receiving the gifts decide which one of them was the most valuable. First Loki presented the gifts from the Sons of Ivaldi. When he pressed the skein of golden hair against Sif's scalp, it took root at once—and when she had run her fingers through it several times and looked at it long and hard in her mirror, she declared herself satisfied and Loki forgiven.

To Frey, Loki presented the little dragon-ship, which he called Skidbladnir, and declared that it could be folded down small enough to fit in Frey's pouch or unfolded large enough to carry a small army.

What's more, when its sail was raised, the ship even provided its own wind.

Then Loki handed the rune-spear to Odin.

"Well, it's a fine-looking spear, Loki, but I have many fine spears in my armory. Does it have any special properties?"

"Indeed, it does, Odin. The spear is called Gungnir, and when you cast it over the heads of an advancing army, fear and confusion will strike the warriors and they will be unable to fight."

"Hmm, that *is* impressive. And now, Brokk, what gifts do you bring us?"

"For you, Odin, my brother, Eitri, has fashioned this arm-ring, which is called Draupnir."

"It *is* extremely well crafted, Brokk, but my treasury is full of arm-rings. Is there anything special about Draupnir?"

"Only this—that every ninth night it will produce eight more rings just like itself. So long as you have Draupnir, you can never be poor."

"Well, there certainly is something to be said for that. What do you have for Frey?"

"For Frey, I have brought this golden boar, who is called Gullinbursti. Frey can ride him through the air or over water, and do so as easily at night as in daytime because the boar casts its own light." Needless to say, Frey was as delighted with the boar as he was with the expandable dragon-ship.

"Finally, my brother, Eitri, and I give to Thor this hammer, called Mjöllnir. It may not seem much to look at, but it will never fail to strike whatever he throws it at . . . and it will always return to his hand after it hits."

Then Odin, Frey, and Thor took counsel together to decide which of these gifts was the best. When they had decided, Odin stood before Loki and Brokk and declared: "Each of these gifts is special in its own unique way, and it would be nearly impossible to declare one superior to the others in craftsmanship alone. However, we have decided that the hammer, Mjöllnir, will help Thor keep the giants out of Asgard . . . and, therefore, it is the most precious gift to us. It would seem, Brokk, that Loki's head belongs to you now."

Loki gulped and pleaded with the Dwarf: "You know, Brokk, I really have more need of my head than you do. Would you be willing to let me ransom it back from you for a pile of gold?"

"No chance, Loki, it's your head I want!"

"You'll have to catch me first," cried Loki as he leaped out through a window.

Unwilling to have the judgment of his court mocked, Odin sent Thor after Loki to fetch him back . . . which Thor promptly did. The Thunder God forced the Trickster to his knees and, grasping Loki's hair in one hand, pulled his head back so Brokk could more easily cut it off.

"Wait a minute, wait a minute," gasped Loki. "It's true that you're entitled to my head, Brokk, but you can't have even the smallest part of my neck. It wasn't part of the wager."

Well, Loki thought he had fooled Brokk with this fine point of law, but the Dwarf had the last laugh: "Perhaps not, Loki, but since I do own your head, the least I can do is to seal your lying lips."

So saying, Brokk took the awl his brother used for piercing leather and poked a row of holes in Loki's lips. Then the Dwarf took a strong leather thong and methodically laced the Trickster's lips together, while Loki protested bitterly.

"Hey, you can't do this to me. Stop it, I tell you. Stop . . mmph, mmph."

Loki sulked off while everyone in the hall enjoyed a good laugh at his discomfort. With a great effort, the Trickster managed to tear the thong out of his lips. But the wounds healed badly and they left permanent scars on his once handsome face. This is just *too* much, Loki thought, and he vowed to get even . . . someday.

The Theft of Thor's Hammer

The giants succeed in stealing Mjöllnir, Thor's magic hammer, and it's up to Loki and the Thunder God to bring it back to Asgard.

It did not take Thor long after he had acquired his mighty hammer, Mjöllnir, before he set off on a giant-and-troll hunting foray to the East. Until he got his new weapon, the Thunder God had been viewed by the giants mostly as a dangerous annoyance. With Mjöllnir's potential to deal death at a distance, however, Thor's name became a household word in Jötunheim . . . something to frighten little giants who misbehaved. "You'd better look out or Thor Redbeard will get you!" their mothers would say.

Well, one morning when Thor awoke and reached down beside his bed to pick up Mjöllnir, he failed to find the hammer. Arising, Thor hastily searched the room . . . but to no avail. Mjöllnir was nowhere to be seen.

"Sif, Sif, wake up!" Thor shouted, shaking his sleeping wife's shoulders.

The lovely blonde goddess stretched and yawned: "What's the matter, Thor, dear?"

"I can't find Mjöllnir anywhere. Where did you put my hammer?"

"Where did *I* put it? Oh, you men can never find anything." Sif rolled her eyes. "Here, let me look for it."

But when Sif's eagle eyes also failed to find the missing hammer, panic began to set in. Just then, Loki strolled past their window, whistling merrily to himself. With a shout, Thor jumped through the window, grabbed the Trickster by the shoulders, and shook him until his teeth rattled. Thor shouted: "You've gone too far this time, Loki. Stealing Mjöllnir just isn't funny. Now, where did you put it?"

"The hammer is missing?" Loki gulped, when Thor stopped shaking the Trickster long enough to let him speak. "Well, I know I didn't do it . . . oh, dear, I'll bet it was one of the giants!"

"Hmm," mused Thor, "if it wasn't you, then you're probably right about who has Mjöllnir. But how can we be sure?"

"I know," said Loki, "Freyja has a feathered cloak that lets her change into a falcon and fly throughout the Nine Worlds. If she will lend me her cloak, I'll fly to Jötunheim and see what I can discover."

"Good idea," agreed Thor, and the two of them rushed off to Sessrumnir, Freyja's spacious hall, to seek the help of the Love Goddess. When they arrived, she was running a comb through her long golden tresses.

"Ninety-seven, ninety-eight, ninety-nine, one-hundred. There, that should do it." Freyja put down her comb and admired herself in her mirror. "A woman always needs to look her best."

Turning to face Thor and Loki, Freyja asked: "And what brings you fellows here this morning?"

"Somebody has stolen Mjöllnir," Thor blurted, "so may Loki borrow your falcon cloak to see if it was the giants?"

"Oh, dear, the hammer is missing?" Freyja gasped, raising a hand to her mouth. "Of course Loki may borrow my cloak—I'd lend it to him even if it were made of silver or gold."

As soon as the goddess placed the cloak in Loki's hands, he swept it over his shoulders and, as it settled in place, muttered a magical incantation. As the spell began to take hold, the Trickster's body shrank, his legs shortened, his toes became talons, and his arms twisted up behind his back and grew feathers. In less time than it took to describe the transformation, where Loki had stood, a giant falcon now appeared.

With a *skree*-ing cry, the falcon launched himself into the air and sped through the open door. Soaring high into the sky, he circled once, then set his course for Jötunheim. So swiftly did he fly, that in no time at all Loki found himself circling above the great hall of the giant king Thrym.

As luck would have it, the king himself was sitting on a bench just outside the hall, braiding a leash for one of his hunting dogs. Loki settled down on the limb of a nearby tree where he could get a closer look at Thrym, and perhaps learn something. Much to the Trickster's chagrin, however, the giant not only noticed him but recognized that he was no ordinary falcon.

"That's no bird's eye I see peering at me," mused Thrym. "My guess is that you're Loki in disguise. How goes it with the gods, Loki; how goes it with the elves?"

"It goes ill with the gods, Thrym, and ill with the elves. Thor's hammer has been stolen. Do you know where it is?" Loki did not believe in beating about the bush.

"Of course I know where it is," the giant king stated emphatically. "I stole the hammer and hid it eight leagues deep. The gods will never get it back, unless . . . ."

"Unless what, Thrym?" Loki queried eagerly.

"Unless they give me Freyja for my bride."

"Oh, I'm sure she's going to love to hear that," the Trickster muttered.

"As well she should. Being my wife will be quite an honor for her," the giant responded, clearly having missed the sarcasm that Loki intended. "But I'm not a very patient fellow, Loki, so if my bride isn't here for the wedding nine days hence, my warriors and I may just have to come up to Asgard to fetch her . . . and that dratted hammer won't be there to stop us. Is that clear?"

"Oh, I understand, Thrym, really I do . . . and I'll be sure to tell the gods what you said, just as soon as I get back to Asgard." And off he flew.

When Loki arrived in Asgard, he found Thor so beside himself with worry that the Thunder God almost didn't let the Trickster have time to reverse the spell on the falcon cloak before demanding to know what Loki had found out.

"It is true, Thor, that Thrym took Mjöllnir and has hidden it well, but he is willing to return the hammer . . . if Freyja will be his bride."

The Thunder God turned to the Love Goddess and demanded: "You heard him, Freyja. Get your bridal gown on, and I'll take you to Jötunheim in my goat cart for your wedding. The sooner we get Mjöllnir back, the better."

"Just you wait a minute, Thor. If you think I'm going to marry some smelly old giant, you'd better think again. I have my reputation to think of." And with that, she grew so enraged that her famous golden necklace, the Brisingamen, burst apart.

At this point, when it was clear that Freyja would have nothing to do with the wedding idea, Heimdall—who had joined the group—spoke up: "Well, you know, Thor, you could always dress up in Freyja's bridal gown yourself. Those giants are too stupid to know the difference."

Thor's face turned beet red. "What? Me dress up like a girl? No way! The guys would never let me live it down." He crossed his brawny arms and sulked.

"Don't be too hasty, Thor," cautioned Loki. "Much as I hate to admit that Heimdall could have a worthwhile idea, I think he has hit on something this time." When Thor continued to balk, the Trickster added: "If you'll agree to do this, I'll dress up as your bridesmaid."

Reluctantly, Thor consented to go along with the masquerade. Altering Freyja's dress to fit him was no easy task, for his figure and Freyja's could not have been less alike. Still, stuff the Thunder God into the dress they finally did . . . but when the gods beheld Thor's face, glowering through his thick red beard, not even the most optimistic of them truly believed the giants would be fooled for long.

"I know how to solve this problem," Loki chortled, and he promptly wrapped the bridal veil around Thor's head, completely obscuring his features from view.

By then, the Trickster had donned a bridesmaid's dress, so he and Thor clambered aboard the Thunder God's goat cart and rattled off toward Jötunheim.

When they arrived and entered Thrym's hall, Thor and Loki found that the assembled giants were already seated awaiting the sumptuous wedding feast and the ceremony that was to follow. The party from Asgard was escorted to the head table and seated on either side of the giant king who, after greeting his bride and her attendant, signaled for the banquet to begin.

It seems to be the nature of things that some persons lose their appetites when they are nervous and upset, while others in a like situation will stuff themselves. Thor was of the latter group. He consumed a whole roasted ox and eight salmon, and drained three large horns of mead. This would have been a gargantuan meal for even a giant maid—let alone a goddess—and Thrym scratched his head in amazement.

"My goodness, what a huge appetite she has!" the giant king exclaimed.

Fearful that Thrym might become suspicious of his bride's true identity, Loki hastened to reassure him: "You must realize, oh king, that Freyja has not eaten for eight days, so anxious has she been to become your wife."

"Well, isn't that sweet!" Thrym declared, beaming broadly. "I just think I'll steal a little kiss."

But when the king began to pull the veil away from Thor's face, two fiery red eyes glared back at him.

"My, what red eyes she has!" he gasped as he jerked his hand back and leaned away from Thor.

"That's because Freyja hasn't slept a wink for the past eight nights, so eager has she been for your love," improvised Loki.

"Well, if that's the way she feels," said Thrym, "I see no reason to delay the ceremony any longer. We'll hold the wedding right now, then she and I can go off and get better acquainted, while the rest of you enjoy the feast. Someone fetch the hammer!"

In those days, the hammer of Thor—or an amulet made in that shape—was placed in the bride's lap during the wedding vows, presumably to insure that the union would be a fertile one.

When Mjöllnir was placed in Thor's lap, his right hand grasped its handle while his left hand gripped the bridal veil. Ripping the veil from his head, the Thunder God leapt to his feet and raised the hammer above his shoulder.

"At last!" Thor shouted, as he shook Mjöllnir menacingly at the crowd.

The face of every giant in the hall turned ashen, for they had all left their weapons outside . . . and here stood their deadliest enemy, armed with the one weapon they most feared. Time seemed to stand still for a moment, then with an outburst of shouts and yells, the terrified giants all scrambled to leave the hall at once. And, of course, they only managed to get in each other's way, which kept them milling around like a herd of crazed cattle while the Thunder God picked them off one by one. Mjöllnir never missed its target, and the hammer promptly flew back into Thor's waiting hand. In no time at all, there wasn't a single giant left alive in the hall.

Briskly rubbing his hands together, Thor observed: "You know, Loki, there's nothing like killing giants to work up a fellow's appetite. What do you say we finish up this banquet, then head on home to Asgard?"

And that's exactly what they did.

The Courtship of Gerd

Frey, the Vanir sun god, falls madly in love with the lovely giantess Gerd, but he is too lovesick to court her. His servant, Skirnir, must save the day.

I misdoubted the whole affair from the very beginning. But when your status in the household of a god is that of a servant, your role is to carry out your lord's commands . . . regardless of your own misgivings. And we Elves are well known for keeping our opinions to ourselves; it adds to the aura of mystery that others perceive surrounding us.

Still, I might have ventured to ask what was troubling my lord Frey, already deeply melancholy, had it not been likely to render him ill-tempered as well. We had practically grown up together, for I became his servant-companion as soon as he was old enough to need one— and it was only fitting that the overlord of Alfheim be served by an Elf-chief's son. In all the ensuing years, I had not seen Frey in such a state . . . so I concluded that discretion was the better part of valor, at least until he indicated a desire to talk.

Alas, my discretion was not a luxury I was to enjoy for long. Frey's refusal to eat or drink, as well as his all-pervasive moodiness, soon came to the attention of his father, Njörd. I don't know if Njörd tried to speak with Frey—and failed—or if the old fellow just didn't feel comfortable enough about having a father-son talk even to try. In any event, early one morning Njörd summoned me into his presence and, having determined that I didn't know what ailed his "boy," ordered me to find out. I respectfully expressed my doubts about encountering anything more than an angry outburst, but Njörd was adamant . . . so I could demur no further, and I agreed to do as he bade me.

*   *   *

"Frey, my friend, what ails you so?" I queried after my soft knock on the door of his bed-closet drew a terse "Go away!"

"I don't want to talk about it," Frey muttered . . . and the door remained closed.

Presuming on our long friendship, I persisted. "Frey, we've known each other since boyhood and have always shared everything, the bad times as well as the good. You've got to talk to someone about your troubles, or you're just going to fade away. Won't you let me help you?"

The door to the bed-closet slowly swung open, and Frey sat up on the edge of his bed. "I guess you're right, Skirnir, but I feel so miserable that I'm no fit company for anyone. I can't eat and I can't sleep for thinking about her." He pushed back his shock of golden hair with both hands.

Her? I pounced on the word. "What 'her' are you talking about, and why should the very thought of her be making you sick?"

"Oh, Skirnir, I'm in love! I'm in love with Gerd Gymirsdatter." And Frey sighed deeply.

"Gymir the Hill Giant?" I intoned the name incredulously. "When did all this happen? I didn't think you'd visited Jötunheim in years."

"I haven't, but I saw her in a vision from Hlidskjalf. She had just stepped out of the door of her father's hall and held out her arms as if greeting the day. So white were her shining arms, they lit the sky and sea. Could any woman be more beautiful?"

"She certainly sounds lovely, the way you describe her. But, by all that's holy, my lord, whatever possessed you to sit on Odin's high throne? You know that the All-Father has forbidden that privilege to any save himself. Disaster is sure to follow this act."

"It already has, Skirnir, it already has. No punishment that Odin could mete out would make me feel worse than I already do. If I can't have Gerd as my wife, I'll die. I mean that with all my heart, Skirnir. Life just wouldn't be worth living without her." Frey paused. "I wonder if Loki knew what was going to happen when he encouraged me to sit on Hlidskjalf . . . 'Go ahead and do it, Frey, nobody will ever know,' he said."

"Loki talked you into this foolishness?" I was horrified. "Oh, Frey, how could you have trusted anything that sly fox said? You know he loves nothing better than to cause discord among the gods."

"I know, I know. But a part of me was curious about what Odin can see from his throne, so it didn't take too much persuasion to convince me." Frey sighed. "Still, my foolishness and Loki's malice aside, the fact remains that I sat, I saw, and I was smitten. You did say you wanted to help me, my friend?"

"I did, my lord, and I still do. But how?" I replied, perplexed.

"Go to Jötunheim, to Gymir's steading, and win the bright-armed maiden for me. I told you I can't live without her." Frey's eyes met mine pleadingly.

"But surely you could court her better yourself. Why would you want me to go?" That I found the prospect distasteful my voice undoubtedly betrayed.

"The gods are sure to disapprove of such a marriage and would stop me from going. And the giants consider me an enemy, so bloodshed would ensue long before we could get around to talk of wooing and wedding. The gods pay little attention to your comings and goings, and the giants wouldn't see you as a threat. You would be the ideal messenger to plead my cause." When I hesitated, he went on, "Please say you'll do this for me . . . if you're successful, I'll reward you beyond your wildest dreams." Frey held out both arms in supplication.

"Gold and jewels weigh but little when friendship is in the balance, my lord," I replied somewhat stiffly, offended that Frey might think he needed to buy my loyalty. "But I will ask for the loan of your horse and your sword—the one that fights giants by itself—that I might defend myself if the wooing goes badly and Gymir becomes violent."

Frey grasped my forearms excitedly. "Then you'll go, Skirnir? I knew I could count on you. Bloody Hoof and my sword are at your disposal . . . and anything else you need. Can you leave at once?"

His excitement thawed me. "As soon as Bloody Hoof can be saddled, and I can pack my saddlebags, we'll be on our way."

"Thank you again, best of friends . . . and with my life in the balance, I know you won't take 'No' for an answer—from either Gerd or her father."

"Fear not, Frey . . . I won't."

*　　　*　　　*

The ride through the misty mountains to Jötunheim was uneventful enough until Bloody Hoof and I drew near to Gymir's steading, where a flickering glow caught my eye. At first I thought that Gymir's hall itself was ablaze, but when I came within sight of my goal I saw that the entire steading was barred to the outer world by a wall of flame—save for a towering stone gateway opposite the hall. But there would be no easy access through that portal, for chained to either side of the gateway was a savage hound that growled fiercely and strained at its binding when it caught sight of my horse and me.

I reined in Bloody Hoof and, espying a shepherd sitting beneath a nearby tree, inquired: "Tell me, good fellow, how is one supposed to get past those hounds to reach Gymir's hall? I have come a long way to speak with his daughter, Gerd."

The herdsman was silent for a moment, sucking his lip pensively. Then, with something approaching a twinkle in his rheumy eyes, he replied: "Weel, yew see, sor, thet's sorta the point, ain't it? Strangers—lak yewrself, beggin' yer pardon, I'm sure—ain't supposed ter get past them dawgs. Thet's why Gymir put them thar, 'tis. Turrible feerce they be, too, sor. 'Twould hate ter see yew and yer nice horsie all torn ter leetle bits. Messy, thet would be." He shook his shaggy grey head slowly and sorrowfully. "Best yew turn about now, sor, and go back home . . . whilst yew can."

I shrugged, without visible emotion, and responded: "One's *wyrd* alone determines what is possible and what is not. One thing I do know—faint heart never knows good luck."

With that I leaned forward, whispered into Bloody Hoof's ear, and we charged forward . . . but not at the gateway and its ferocious guardians. No, we headed directly at the wall of fire and, at what I sensed to be just the critical moment, I tapped the horse's flank and flattened myself against his neck. Bloody Hoof responded by leaping as high and as far through the flames as his stout heart and powerful legs would carry him. And as *wyrd* would have it—though the heat was nigh unto unbearable—neither the horse nor I was harmed.

Thwarted in their role as guardians of the gateway, the two hounds set up an awful howl. Gerd must have heard the commotion from within the hall, for shortly—as I allowed Bloody Hoof to graze on the grass in the courtyard—a serving maid stuck her head out the door to see what was going on. She stared at me, open-mouthed, for a moment, then disappeared back into the hall. Soon Gerd herself appeared, and I must admit that, despite his being lovesick, Frey had not exaggerated her beauty. Being a giantess, Gerd was much bigger-boned than would normally appeal to elvish tastes, but she certainly was a magnificent-looking woman!

This impression was only reinforced when she spoke, for she had a warm, throaty voice. "Who are you, stranger? Are you one of the Aesir, a Van, or perhaps an Elf?"

"I am Skirnir the Elf, fair lady, but I come on behalf of one of the Vanir. My master, Lord Frey, has loved you from afar and wishes to marry you."

"Me, marry one of the gods? Why would I ever want to do that?" Gerd asked incredulously.

"Perhaps my lady would consider Idunn's golden apples of eternal youth a sufficient inducement," I offered.

"I *have* youth and beauty . . . what need have I for Idunn's silly apples?" she retorted.

"Well, one can never have enough gold," I countered. "Would Odin's magic ring, Draupnir, which produces eight gold rings every ninth night, stir your heart?"

"My father's treasure room contains all the gold I could ever need," Gerd replied haughtily.

By the red beard of Thor, beauty or not, this giantess was stubborn beyond belief and arrogant to boot! She seemed to have no notion of the great honor Frey was offering her. Having to bargain with her like a fishmonger was galling, yet Frey had admonished me not to take "No" for an answer, and so far that was all I had heard from Gerd. Normally Elves are the very soul of patience—and the thought of coercing another being is abhorrent to us—but with Frey pining away and my having the responsibility to save him, I'm afraid I violated the Alfar code. For which there'll be a price to pay, I'm sure.

"Beware of overweening pride, lady. Do you see this sword?" And I half drew Frey's blade from its scabbard.

"What is that sword to me? Are . . . are you *threatening* me with it?" Gerd stared at me as if the very idea was too ridiculous to be believed.

"Indeed, I am," I replied coldly and with as much dignity as I could muster. "Unless you agree to marry Lord Frey, I am going to smite your head from your body."

Folding her arms and cocking her head, she considered me skeptically. "Neither my head nor my body would be of much use to your master if they were separated, would they? No, Skirnir, your threat is an empty one."

Curse the woman, she was shrewder than I'd anticipated. Curse the woman? Ah ha, that might be the answer. If the final death held no fear for her, perhaps a living death might. That an Elf would even consider such a thing reveals how desperate I had become. Extracting a flat, narrow birch wand from my saddlebag, I drew my belt knife and began to carve a series of arcane symbols on the flattened surface.

Gerd eyed my actions suspiciously and finally asked: "Tell me, Skirnir, what *are* you up to?"

"You have tried my patience too far, lady," I replied. "Do you see this wand I hold in my hand? I have scratched four curse runes upon it—one each for loathing, lust, trolls, and filth. If you do not agree at once to marry Frey, I will invoke these curses upon your head. Would you hear what they are?"

Warily, Gerd nodded and silently awaited my proclamation.

"Well, then," I began, "should I invoke these curses, you shall be condemned to sit alone on a barren mountain peak facing Hel's Gate, barely able to swallow food that will have become as loathsome to you as a slithery knot of serpents. Your comely face shall become so repulsive that everyone will avoid your company, and you shall be plagued with unbearable sadness and constant weeping. Should you visit the Frost Giants, their wee ones will pursue you, pinching and pulling, all the day long as—bent and broken in body—you hobble about the hall."

I paused for breath, and to judge the impact on Gerd of what I had said. Her fists were clenched, her lips parted, and worry lines had appeared at the corners of her deep blue eyes, so I went on.

"Odin and Thor, and even Frey, shall be furious with you, all three tribes of giants shall despise you, and the joy and love of men shall be denied you. You shall be wracked with overwhelming lust, yet none shall agree to marry you save an ugly three-headed troll! That's right, you'll be forced to mate with gruesome old Hrimgrimnir in the bowels of Niflheim where, in a dim grotto beneath the root of the Tree, drooling slaves shall serve you goat urine—the only drink you shall ever have again."

Gerd shuddered and gulped. A part of me was ashamed of what I was putting her through, but I steeled myself to complete the task.

"Now is the moment of decision, lady. If you would stay the curses, agree to be Frey's wife, and I will scrape the wood clean of the runes. If you will not, I have but to say one word and the curses will begin their work. Once said, that word cannot be taken back, and no power in the Nine Worlds can overturn the curses it sets in motion." I wasn't altogether certain that my last statement was completely true, but I doubted if Gerd would know that.

Gerd raised the palms of her hands in surrender and swallowed hard. "Enough, Skirnir, enough. I yield to your threats, and I shall marry your master . . . though what happiness for either of us can grow out of such a courtship, I know not."

Turning toward the hall, Gerd clapped her hands to fetch her serving maid, who made such a rapid appearance that she surely must have been eavesdropping from just within the portal. Her mistress sent her off on an errand, and shortly the maid returned bearing a crystal goblet filled with golden mead. After sipping from one side of the cup, Gerd held it out to me with these words: "With this cup, I pledge myself to wed Frey. Drink you now, Skirnir, as his spokesman, to seal the pledge."

"With all my heart, Lady Gerd." I downed the rest of the drink and handed the goblet to the serving maid. "Now tell me—for Lord Frey is sure to ask—just when and where the marriage shall take place?"

Gerd sighed: "Tell Frey that I will meet him at the trysting glade in the forest of Barri nine nights hence. There shall we be wed."

I bowed to her and remounted Bloody Hoof for my ride home. As I passed through the gateway—the hounds having since been tethered on short chains—I looked back and extended my arm in salute to a brave and noble lady.

Gerd waved back and called out: "My father will send word of the bride-price before the wedding. Farewell, Skirnir."

*   *   *

Of the long ride back, there is little to say. No sooner had I come in sight of Frey's abode than he rushed out to greet me and demand news of my mission.

"Skirnir, Skirnir, what news have you for me? Will Gerd marry me?"

After I had dismounted and handed Bloody Hoof's reins to a stable boy, I replied: "She will, indeed, my lord . . . nine nights hence in the forest of Barri."

Frey's mouth gaped. "Nine nights? One night without her seems like a year, two an eternity. How can I possibly wait for nine?"

*   *   *

But he did, and the wedding took place as planned. And, as time passes, Gerd even seems to be happy being Frey's wife. He, of course, is beside himself with joy.

Then why do I continue to have misgivings? Well, remember the bride-price? When Gymir sent his message, he demanded Frey's sword as Gerd's bride-price. He said it would be a token of good faith on Frey's part; after all, if Frey were going to marry a giantess, why would he need a sword that slew giants by itself . . . that would hardly be a friendly way to treat his new wife's kinfolk!

Gymir's argument sounds reasonable on the surface—and Frey wanted Gerd so badly he would have given her father his right arm if he'd asked for it—but giants *are* giants, and that sword was second only to Thor's hammer as a defense against an invasion from Jötunheim . . . and now it's gone. I can't speak for others in Asgard, but I sleep much less easily these nights.

Loki's Children

What happens when you cross Loki with a troll woman? Their three children—a sea dragon, a two-faced daughter, and a giant wolf—pose unique threats to Asgard.

For a time, the marriage of Loki and Sigyn was a happy one, and they even had two sons, Nari and Vali. But Loki was not the sort of fellow who could ever be content with only one woman—no matter how beautiful, affectionate, or loyal. So it should not come as a surprise to learn that when he encountered the troll-woman Angrboda in the Ironwood, during his wanderings in Jötunheim, Loki succumbed to her charms. Not that her thick, leathery hide, meter-long nose, and bent, shuffling gait would have appealed to every man—but Loki had a taste for the exotic.

At any rate, Loki visited Angrboda often enough that she bore him three children—three *very* strange children. But, then, what would you have expected if you crossed Loki with a troll? One son was a giant serpent (or limbless dragon) called Jörmungand, another son was a talking wolf they named Fenris, and their daughter they called Hel.

When the gods learned of the existence of Loki's children—and who their mother was—they became uneasy. And when a prophecy suggested that great misfortune would come upon the gods because of these children, Odin secretly sent a group of gods into Jötunheim on a special mission. There they seized Jörmungand, Hel, and Fenris Wolf, and brought them back to Asgard, where they could be raised under the watchful eyes of the Aesir until Odin decided what to do with Loki's strange children.

Jörmungand proved to have a great appetite, and he grew so rapidly that it was not long before he was large enough that he could have swallowed one of the gods, if he so chose. Assuming that this possibility was what the prophecy had warned against, Odin carried the Serpent up on top of the ramparts of Asgard and hurled him out into space.

So powerful was Odin's throw that Jörmungand cleared the outer limits of Asgard altogether, and tumbled into the great ocean that surrounded Midgard. There his insatiable appetite—and ever-increasing length—led him to seek ever larger prey until nothing less than a whale could satisfy him . . . and that but for a time. Eventually, the Midgard Serpent (as he came to be called) grew so long that he extended all the way around Midgard and bumped into his own tail, which he promptly bit down upon.

Hel posed a different sort of problem for the Aesir. One side of her face and form she had inherited from her father (and Loki was a handsome fellow), but the other side was all too gruesomely trollish like her mother. Those gods who sat on her good side at meals found Hel to be a tolerable table companion, but those who sat on her other side had trouble keeping their food down . . . and usually left the table at the first opportunity. It is from Loki's daughter, almost certainly, that we get the expression that someone "looks like Hel."

Odin knew that he had to get Hel safely out of Asgard before half of the Aesir refused to eat in the hall, but he felt it would be ungentlemanly to simply throw her over the wall as he had her brother Jörmungand. Suddenly he was struck with a brilliant idea.

"Hel, I've been watching you since you've been living here in Asgard, and I've really been impressed with your dignity and calmness. So impressed, in fact, that I think you can help me out with a little problem I have."

"And what problem is that, Odin?" Hel responded quietly.

"Well, as I'm sure you know by now, the spirits of humans who die in combat are brought up to Valhalla by my Valkyries to spend eternity here." Hel nodded, and waited for Odin to continue. "They're not my problem, Hel; the 'straw deaths' are. They're the ones who die in childbirth, or from illness, or just plain old age. Their spirits are wandering aimlessly about in the nameless depths below Niflheim, and what they need is to be organized. How about it, Hel? Would you like to rule over them? Why, we can even name their realm after you, if you like. What do you say?"

Hel laid a long, white finger on the corner of her mouth, and pondered aloud: "Hel, Queen of the Dead! Yes, I like the sound of that. And it gives my life purpose. Thank you, Odin. When may I begin my duties?"

"Oh, the sooner the better, I should think. We'll arrange transportation for you immediately so you can meet your subjects and start getting them organized."

And as Hel departed, Odin could barely keep from laughing aloud at the thought that he had just sent her unsettling presence as far from Asgard as it was possible to go in the Nine Worlds.

As long as Fenris was only a cub, the Aesir did not feel greatly threatened by the wolf's presence. Still, the prophecy's ominous warning hung over them, so only the god Tyr was entirely comfortable hand-feeding young Fenris. The wolf shared his brother's ravenous appetite and rapid growth, hence it wasn't very long before Fenris was as large as a horse . . . and still growing. At that point, the Aesir realized that Fenris was big enough to be a threat to their very lives, and they demanded that Odin do something about him.

The simplest solution, of course, would have been to kill Fenris on the spot. But, having allowed the wolf into Asgard and having fed him, that would have violated the law of hospitality, one of the most sacred laws of the Viking Age. No, Odin needed a more subtle approach to deal with Fenris Wolf.

One day, Odin approached the wolf and declared: "Fenris, you are—without a doubt—the biggest, strongest, smartest wolf in all the Nine Worlds."

"I know, I know," rumbled the flattered, but immodest, wolf.

"So it really bothers me," continued Odin, "that you don't get the honor and glory you so richly deserve."

"It is sad," sighed Fenris. Then he shrugged his lupine shoulders and said: "But what's a wolf to do?"

"I think what is needed," declared Odin, "is a demonstration."

"A demonstration?" queried Fenris, perking up his ears. "Just what did you have in mind?"

"Well, if you were to let us tie you up with a thick rope, then you could break it, and everyone would praise you for your strength."

"Sounds like a good idea to me. When can we do it?"

"There's no time like the present," opined Odin. "Just let me get a rope, and assemble the other gods so they can watch you show your strength."

Soon all of the Aesir had gathered in a large circle around Fenris to watch as several of the gods wrapped the wolf in a stout anchor rope from one of their dragon-ships. After tying the final knot, they barely had time to step back and admire their handiwork before

Fenris expanded his mighty chest. The rope snapped asunder with a noisy crack, then slid from the wolf's body.

"Hrr-hrr, hrr-hrr," growl-laughed the wolf.

"Humph," retorted Odin, shaking his head from side to side. "That was far too easy to win you much honor, Fenris. You need to break free from something far more challenging . . . a chain, perhaps."

"Oh, very well," huffed Fenris, and he allowed himself to be bound with a huge iron chain, each link of which was as long as the palm of a man's hand. But once the wolf exerted his strength, the chain lasted little longer than the rope had. Pieces of broken chain sailed in all directions, scattering the onlookers.

"Hrr-hrr, hrr-hrr," growl-laughed Fenris once more.

Appalled by the ease with which the wolf had shattered the great chain, the Aesir muttered uneasily—and all heads turned as one toward Odin.

"Well," said the All-Father in feigned disgust, "it seems they just don't make chains like they used to. I'm really sorry, Fenris, that we couldn't provide you with a chain worthy of your prowess. I'll tell you what . . . give me a day or two to see if I can't find some other binding that might truly test your mettle."

"All right," sniffed the wolf, "I can wait."

*   *   *

At Odin's command, Frey's servant-companion, Skirnir, hastened to Svartalfheim. There he persuaded some of the Dwarves to craft a very special binding for Fenris Wolf. Special it was because of the unique ingredients that went into its making—the noise a cat makes when it walks, the beard of a woman, the roots of a mountain, the sinews of a bear, the breath of a fish, and the spittle of a bird. When the Dwarves were finished, they held in their hands Gleipnir, a cord that was deceptively slender—but actually the strongest binding the Nine Worlds had ever seen.

When Skirnir returned to Asgard bearing Gleipnir, Odin immediately called together Fenris Wolf and the Aesir for the third, and hopefully final, test. The wolf looked at Gleipnir with a skeptical eye, then sniffed at it inquiringly.

"Snf, snf. Magic! I smell magic," declared Fenris, baring his teeth and backing away from the cord. "Are you trying to trick me?"

"Now, now, Fenris, there's nothing to get excited about," Odin said soothingly. "None of the ordinary bindings challenged you in the least, so I had to find *something* that would let you win great fame. What's a little magic to strength like yours? Surely you weren't thinking of backing out, were you?"

"Well, no, I suppose not—I wouldn't want you Aesir to accuse me of cowardice. But just to make sure that the test is really fair, I'll only go through with it if one of you will put his hand between my jaws until I am free again. Agreed?"

The Aesir avoided the wolf's gaze and looked at each other. Knowing that they did, indeed, plan to trick Fenris, who among them would willingly sacrifice his hand for the binding of the wolf? Sensing the gods' hesitation, and growing increasingly suspicious of their intentions, Fenris grew more and more agitated . . . and thus more dangerous. Just then, Tyr, the god whom Fenris most trusted, stepped forward.

"I'll do it," said Tyr—more calmly than he felt—and placed his right hand in the wolf's mouth. Fenris clamped his jaws shut on the god's hand—gently but firmly. Then the Aesir wound Gleipnir round and round the wolf's body before finally tying his legs together, too. Fenris looked altogether helpless—but he had looked that way after the rope and chain had been secured, too, so everyone held his breath.

Fenris took a deep breath and flexed his mighty muscles, but try as he might, he could not budge the magic cord. The wolf was truly bound at last, and one look at the faces of the circle of Aesir told Fenris that they had no intention of ever releasing him. Enraged, Fenris bit down hard, then—as Tyr staggered away clutching the bloody stump of his wrist—the wolf flung the god's hand away with a violent flip of his head.

Fenris opened wide his mouth, and howled his frustration and despair to all the Nine Worlds: "Aroo-oo-oo-oo-oo-oo-oo-oo-oo."

As the last echo of his mournful cry faded, Fenris opened his mouth to howl again. But one of the Aesir seized a sword and thrust the blade upright into the wolf's mouth so he that could never close it again. At last, Fenris Wolf was truly helpless—unable to move, unable to howl, unable even to swallow. And thus shall he remain until Ragnarök, the Doom of the Gods, when all bindings shall be loosed . . . and the Wolf shall go forth to swallow even Odin himself!

PART TWO: THE OLDEST TROLL TALE

The nature of trolls is discussed at length in Chapter Eight of the second section in this book. The earliest recorded troll story does not come from a Scandinavian source at all, but rather from the Old English classic, *Beowulf,* which scholars feel probably was composed just prior to the Viking Age. Although Grendel and his mother are not specifically called trolls in the poem, they fit the description remarkably well. For this reason, and since the story has a Scandinavian setting (Denmark), I feel justified in including their tale in this collection.

Grendel and His Mother

If they look like trolls, smell like trolls, and act like trolls, what else can they be? Two fearsome trolls were terrorizing Denmark. Could the hero Beowulf subdue them?

Long, long ago, when Hrothgar was the most renowned king of the Danes, he decided to build a great feasting hall, the likes of which might not be seen outside of Asgard. And, as the king commanded, so it was done. The ablest carpenters of that day built the massive hall, and the most skilled craftsmen decorated and furnished it. Hrothgar was delighted with his new hall, which he called Heorot, and soon he was giving fabulous feasts for his faithful followers, whom he gifted with arm-rings of silver and gold.

Alas, the merriment issuing forth from Hrothgar's hall aroused the ire of a fearsome fen-dweller, the terrible night-prowler called Grendel. Manlike he was in general form, but larger and stronger by far, and gripped by a gnawing lust for human flesh. Grendel waited until all was quiet within the hall, when the warriors lay deep in drunken dreams—then entering Heorot, he fell upon them and slew thirty of Hrothgar's finest fellows. Half he gobbled up on the spot, and half he dragged back to his loathsome lair in the fens to save for a midnight meal.

The next morning the evidence of Grendel's rapacious raid was plain to see. The gruesome remains of those he had eaten, and on the floor the huge, bloody footprints, announced the awful author of that audacious attack. That very night, Grendel struck again . . . and thereafter no Dane would spend a night beneath Heorot's vaulted roof. The mightiest of earthly halls lay abandoned.

For twelve long years Grendel terrorized the land of the Danes. None dared venture far from home after dark for fear the dreaded night-prowler might suddenly rise up out of the mist and devour him.

Then, at last, Beowulf, the bravest of the Geats, a people dwelling in what is now southern Sweden, heard of Hrothgar's bane and resolved to put an end to it. Beowulf and fourteen courageous companions sailed to Denmark and offered their services to Hrothgar, who was only too happy to accept them. And small wonder, for Beowulf was no ordinary man.

In his youth, Beowulf had, on a dare, swum out to sea wearing a chain-mail shirt and carrying his naked sword. Indeed, he remained at sea for five full days and slew nine sea-monsters with his sword before the ocean currents deposited him safely on the shores of Lapland. Could even so fearsome a monster as Grendel hope to stand against such a hero?

That very night, Beowulf and his men took their rest in Heorot, daring Grendel to do his worst. Sure enough, the cruel creature came, burst open the lock on the outer door, and strode into the hall. Seizing one of Beowulf's companions, Grendel broke his neck with one quick twist, drank the life's blood right out of his veins, and then proceeded in just a few great bites to swallow the man's entire body from his head to his toes.

Beowulf had awakened too late to save his comrade, but awaken he did . . . and when Grendel selected him to be the next victim, Beowulf sprang up and grasped the troll's outstretched arm in his iron grip. Grendel gasped in pain . . . never before had he been so thwarted, and as doubt and fear crept into his stunned mind, he tried to pull free from Beowulf and flee the hall. But the hero persisted, and in their ensuing struggle—Grendel to break free, Beowulf to hold him fast—every bench in the hall was overturned, and its very timbers shaken.

Beowulf's men tried to help him by hacking at Grendel with their swords, but his skin was magically protected against any blade. With one final violent wrench, accompanied by a hideous, unearthly scream, Grendel at last tore loose. But as he staggered, bleeding, from the hall, he left his arm behind—still gripped in Beowulf's granite grasp.

At daylight, the men followed Grendel's blood-bedewed trail to the edge of a dark, evil-looking lake—apparently the home to which he had returned to die. The warriors rejoiced at Grendel's demise, and returned to Heorot where they reported the wonderful news. Then, they hung the monster's arm high on the wall to celebrate Beowulf's triumph and their safety.

All seemed to be well, but that very night Grendel's mother appeared in the hall, bent on revenge. Unfortunately, Beowulf was spending the night elsewhere, so he was not on hand to deal with her.

Nonetheless, the brave warriors wielded their weapons and were able to frighten her off . . . but not before she had killed Hrothgar's closest comrade, and taken with her both his corpse and Grendel's blood-encrusted arm.

The next morning, Beowulf led a war band along her back trail, which led straight to the same lake sought out by the dying Grendel. Next to the lake the men found the severed head of their unfortunate comrade, and the lake water seemed to be boiling with blood. Swimming about in the lake were many serpents and sea-dragons, which plunged beneath the waves when the war band winded its battle horn . . . all save one dragon that Beowulf killed with an arrow.

An ordinary man could not have hoped to follow Grendel's mother into her lair beneath the lake, but—as we have said—Beowulf was no ordinary man. Donning his chain-mail shirt and taking in hand his famed war-sword, Hrunting, Beowulf bade his comrades farewell and plunged into the roiling waters.

It is said that it took Beowulf a full day to sink to the bottom of the lake, so deep it was. When he finally reached the bottom, he was grasped immediately in the troll-woman's fearful embrace. So marvelously made was his chain-mail, however, that she was unable to penetrate the armor with her clawlike fingers. Frustrated, she carried him into her cave beneath the lake, where there was no water, and Beowulf could once again take a breath—though the air there was dank and foul.

Breaking loose from her grip, Beowulf swung his sword at Grendel's mother with a mighty stroke. Alas, Hrunting's edge failed to cleave her flesh, and the hero threw the blade from him in disgust. Beowulf leaped to grapple the ogress, supposing he might do to her what he had done to her son. To Beowulf's dismay, Grendel's mother proved to be a better wrestler than her son, and she threw the hero to the floor of the cave. Leaping upon him, she drew her dagger, and only the strength of his chain-mail shirt kept Beowulf's life in his body.

Desperation drove Beowulf to throw her off and, before Grendel's mother could leap on him again, he wrenched down a huge sword that was hanging handily on the cave wall. This sword had been forged by the giants, and no ordinary man could have wielded it. As Grendel's mother charged for the last time, the giants' sword swung in a great arc and swept her head from her body. She fell dead at Beowulf's feet.

Thus passed Grendel's mother, but so potent was her blood that it melted the sword's blade. Thus all that Beowulf bore back with him to the surface of the world was the sword's hilt and the head of Grendel, which the hero had cut from the troll's corpse in the cave before the blade disappeared completely.

PART THREE: THE RING OF DOOM

The tale of a magic ring that carries with it a promise of great wealth or power, as well as a terrible curse, has fascinated northern Europeans and their descendants for ages. The story appears to have had its origin in Scandinavian oral tradition at least as far back as the Viking Age. The earliest written accounts of the Ring of Doom appeared during the thirteenth century in the Icelandic *Eddas* and *Volsunga Saga*, as well as in the Germanic *Nibelungenlied*. Interest in the Ring was revived in the nineteenth century with William Morris's translation and retelling of the *Volsunga Saga*, and, of course, Richard Wagner's awe-inspiring opera cycle, *The Ring of the Nibelungs*. In the twentieth century, J. R. R. Tolkien took the motif of a cursed ring of power and made it a major focus of his novel *The Hobbit* and, especially, of its trilogy sequel, *The Lord of the Rings*.

Few people are aware that the ancient Norse myths tell of two magic rings. One of them, called Draupnir, was an arm-ring fashioned for the god Odin by two dwarvish smiths. Every ninth night it would produce eight more rings just like itself—so obviously it was a source of great wealth for its owner. There was no curse associated with Draupnir, but eventually this ring was sent to the land of the dead on Balder's funeral pyre.

The other ring, Andvaranaut, was a finger-ring belonging to the Dwarf Andvari. It, too, could produce wealth . . . although we are never told precisely how this was done. This is the ring that eventually crossed paths with Sigurd the Volsung, he who has been called the greatest hero of the Ancient North. How the ring Andvaranaut came to be cursed, how it came into Sigurd's possession, and what happened to him because of it lie at the heart of our story. It all began like this . . .

Episode One: Otter's Blood Price

One bright spring morning, Odin, Hoenir, and Loki strode over the rainbow bridge and down into Midgard for a day's wandering. Coming upon a fast-flowing river, they followed it until evening when they came to its source—a beautiful waterfall. While Odin and Hoenir were admiring the waterfall, Loki spotted a large otter sprawled on a boulder below the falls nibbling on a salmon it had just caught.

Well, the temptation was just too great, and picking up a large round stone from the water's edge, Loki threw it with deadly aim—and a certain amount of luck—at the unsuspecting otter. Thwack! The stone struck the poor beast full in the head and killed him on the spot.

"Hoorah," shouted Loki, "two for the price of one. Am I a great rock thrower or aren't I?" And he danced with glee before wading out to bring back his kill.

The trio thought they would have to cook their supper on the riverbank and spend the night sleeping in the woods, but Hoenir spotted a trail leading off through the woods, and above the trees in that direction there was a small column of smoke rising. Surely there must be a farmstead nearby. Carrying the salmon and the otter, they hurried along the path and soon came out of the woods and up to the gate of a very prosperous-looking farm. The farmer was standing by the door of his hall, so Odin greeted him.

"Hail and good-day to you, my good man. Could we trouble you for a night's lodging? We don't come empty-handed . . . we bring a fine salmon and an otter you may have."

The farmer's eyes grew wide, then narrowed as his face took on a grim expression. "Hmm, er, well, I need to consult with my two sons before turning them out of their beds for the night. You just wait right there. I'll be back soon."

And saying this, the farmer—who was really a master magician named Hreidmarr—disappeared into his hall and slammed the door behind him. Odin, Hoenir, and Loki thought this rather peculiar behavior, but not wanting to sleep in the woods, they waited.

Hreidmarr quickly called his two sons, Fafnir and Reginn, to his side and told them that their brother, Otter, had been killed and that his murderers were waiting at the gate wanting supper and a bed for the night.

"I told that boy to be more careful about where he did his shape-changing, but do you suppose he would listen . . . no, not Otter, and now he's dead. Well, we will have our revenge."

So Hreidmarr and his two remaining sons went out to greet their visitors and invite them in for supper and a night's lodging. But once the gods' suspicions were allayed, Hreidmarr cast a powerful spell upon them so they could not resist while Fafnir and Reginn bound them tightly in unbreakable cords.

Odin demanded to know why they were being treated so inhospitably, and Hreidmarr declared that they had killed his other son, Otter, and now they, too, must die.

"But your son wasn't killed out of malice. We had no way of knowing he was not what he seemed to be—just an ordinary otter. Spare our lives and we will pay whatever blood-price you feel is just."

"Well-l-l, since it was something of an accident, I suppose I could accept compensation. I'll tell you what, we'll remove Otter's skin, and if you will fill it full of gold on the inside *and* cover it with gold on the outside, I'll consider that justice has been done. But . . . just to make sure there are no tricks played, two of you will remain here as our 'guests' until the other one brings back the gold."

Well, Odin had no choice but to agree, and since Loki had gotten them into this tight spot to begin with, the All-Father charged the Trickster with gathering the blood-price.

"And do it quickly, Loki. Hoenir and I have no desire to rely on Hreidmarr's hospitality any longer than absolutely necessary. I don't like the way those two sons of his keep fingering their skinning knives and leering at us."

"I'm on my way," said Loki as soon as the spell was lifted, and he dashed off to Svartalfheim, the underground world of the Dwarves. There he searched until he found a silent black lake, and in that lake he wriggled his fingers . . . until they closed upon the gills of a large pike, which Loki jerked up onto the shore. There he held it until—desperate for water—the pike changed into its true form, that of a gray-bearded old Dwarf.

"Well, Andvari, it looks as if I've got you now. And I have no intention of letting you live unless you give me all the gold you own."

Andvari groaned but reluctantly agreed, and bringing forth all of his treasure, he piled it up at Loki's feet. However, when he thought Loki wasn't looking, he slipped a small gold ring into his tunic.

"Oh, no you don't, Andvari. You agreed to ransom your life with all your gold . . . and that includes the ring."

"Please, Loki, please let me keep the ring. It's called Andvaranaut, and it can make more gold. With it, I'll at least have something left; without it I'll have nothing, not even hope."

"Too bad, Andvari. But I'll have *all* your gold or your life. It's your choice."

"Take the ring then, curse you. And I place a curse on the ring, too. It will be the death of anyone who keeps it for himself."

"Well, that's worth knowing. Goodbye, Andvari. May we never meet again." And Loki hurried out of Dwarf land and back to Hreidmarr's farm. There he showed Andvari's gold to Odin, who thought it should be enough to meet their ransom . . . but Odin liked the look of Andvaranaut and decided to keep the ring for himself. Thus the ring was not included when they filled the otterskin full of gold and covered the outside, too. Odin thought they were free to go, but Hreidmarr found that a single whisker still showed through.

"Unless that whisker is covered, you have failed to meet our agreement."

Odin sighed and pulled Andvaranaut from his tunic. "A dead man needs no wealth; a living man can always gain more." And he placed the ring over the whisker, thus completing Otter's blood-price.

Well, the gods wasted no time after that in parting company with Hreidmarr and his two sons, but just as Loki was passing through the gate, he turned back long enough to tell Hreidmarr of Andvari's curse, then scampered off after Odin and Hoenir.

Episode Two: The Coming of Sigurd

It wasn't long before Fafnir and Reginn demanded a share of
Otter's blood-price from their father, and the curse began to work.
The miserly Hreidmarr refused to give either of his sons so much as
a single gold coin, and that night Fafnir ran a sword into their father
as he slept. Reginn wanted half of the gold as his share, but Fafnir
intended to keep it all for himself, so he warned Reginn to leave
before he killed him, too. Then Fafnir gathered up the gold, a sword
called Hrotti, and Hreidmarr's magic helmet (it was called the Helm
of Terror because it struck fear in the hearts of all who looked upon
it). Fafnir carried his treasures up to a large cave on Gnita Heath, and
there he turned himself into a dragon and coiled around the pile of
gold.

As for Reginn, his wanderings brought him at last to the land of
the Danes where he took service as a smith with the mighty King
Hjalprek. When Reginn arrived, he found Hjalprek's court all a-buzz,
for the king's son, Alf, had just returned from a Viking expedition and
brought back with him the very lovely—and very pregnant—Queen
Hjordis, widow of the far-famed Sigmund, last of the Volsung kings.
King Lyngvi, an unsuccessful suitor for the young queen's hand, had
challenged Sigmund and his army to a battle. Although he was the
older man, Sigmund was leading his forces to victory when Odin
appeared on the battlefield and shattered Sigmund's sword on his
spear. The weaponless king soon fell before the onslaught of his
enemies.

That night, Hjordis came and carried off the pieces of Sigmund's
broken sword. When morning dawned, she saw Prince Alf's Viking
fleet about to land and plunder the battlefield, so she traded clothing

and places with her serving maid in order that the Vikings would not know who she was. Quality will show through, however, and Alf was not fooled for long. When Hjordis realized that he had seen through her disguise, she told the prince the whole story and threw herself on his mercy. Alf was fascinated by the tale—as well as by the beauty and spirit of its teller—and he brought Hjordis back to Denmark with him.

King Hjalprek greeted Sigmund's widow with great courtesy, and she lived at his court in all honor until after her baby was born, a lusty boy-child, whom she named Sigurd, as his father would have wanted. It was not very long thereafter that the beautiful widow married Prince Alf, and Sigurd acquired a step-father. Alf never mistreated the boy—in fact, he had relatively little to do with Sigurd's upbringing, for in those days it was the custom for boys of noble birth to learn men's skills from a foster-father. Often the man to whom a boy was fostered was a brother of his mother, but Hjordis had no living brother . . . so when the time came, Sigurd was fostered to Reginn, who over the years had made himself invaluable to the king and impressed everyone with his knowledge and skill.

Reginn became truly fond of the good-natured boy, who was always eager to learn whatever the smith was willing to teach him. And teach him Reginn did, not only weapon's play, but chess, foreign tongues, runelore, and much else to help Sigurd's mind and body grow. But Reginn had never forgotten what his brother Fafnir had done to him, and knowing that a son of Sigmund was sure to grow into a mighty warrior, Reginn sought to hone that warrior-in-the-making into his own personal weapon of vengeance. Fond of the boy he might well be, but revenge ruled Reginn's heart!

So it was that as Sigurd entered young manhood, Reginn began to fill his head with tales of Sigmund's glory . . . and to hint that Sigurd might become greater still.

"It isn't fitting," Reginn purred, "that Sigmund's son should ride a pony. King Hjalprek should give you a war horse."

That sounded like a good idea to the eager young man, who promptly ran off to ask Hjalprek for a steed. The king never denied Sigurd anything, so Hjalprek invited him to visit the king's own herd and choose whichever horse caught Sigurd's fancy. Early the next morning, Sigurd went down by the River Busiltjorn to view the herd that grazed in the meadow there. As he watched the horses in admiration, an old, one-eyed man appeared—as if from nowhere—and asked him why he was there.

When Sigurd explained, the old man replied: "If you will be advised by me, drive the herd into the river. When you see what they do there, then you will know which one to choose."

Sigurd agreed and did as the old man had told him. All of the horses, save one, swam across the river as fast as they could and scrambled out of the icy water. The one that did not, a young gray, took his time and showed no discomfort from the cold. Sigurd was fascinated by this young stallion, all the more so when the old man said: "His name is Grani and he is a descendent of Odin's horse, Sleipnir. Small wonder he is hardier than the rest of this lot. Call him by name and see if he will come to you."

Sigurd did so, and when Grani immediately swam ashore and nuzzled the young man, Sigurd knew he had made a friend for life. After a time, Sigurd turned to the old man to thank him, but Odin—for it was Odin in disguise—had disappeared.

Now that Sigurd had an incomparable war horse, Reginn began to regale him with tales of great wealth. "It isn't right that Sigmund's son should have to beg the King and his son for gold, even if they do give you anything you ask for. If you were to slay the dragon Fafnir and gain his hoard, you'd never have to ask anyone for anything ever again."

"Oh, I'm hardly the one to do that deed," said Sigurd. "I've only just grown out of boyhood, and I've yet to blood my sword on a man. Slaying that old dragon is a task for a far more seasoned warrior than I."

Reginn fixed him with an icy stare and snarled: "A true Volsung would never let a little thing like that stop him when there is a great deed to do and much gold to be won. Now, listen while I tell you the reason why *I* want to see that dragon slain." And Reginn told Sigurd the tale of Otter's blood-price and what Fafnir had done with it. "So if you'll kill Fafnir, you can keep all the gold . . . I just want my revenge!"

Sigurd agreed, but he said that Reginn would need to make him a sword that was equal to the task. The first two that Reginn crafted looked like fine weapons, but their blades shattered when Sigurd smote Reginn's anvil with them. Sigurd then asked his mother, Hjordis, for the pieces of Sigmund's sword, Gram, and when Reginn had finished reforging the broken sword, Sigurd was able to cleave the anvil in two right down to its base. Clearly Gram was strong enough, but Sigurd wondered about the sharpness of its edge.

At Reginn's suggestion, Sigurd and the smith went down by the river. Reginn instructed the young man to thrust the blade into the stream with the edge facing the current. The smith then strode upstream along the bank for nine paces and, turning, tossed a large clump of sheep's wool into the current. As the clump drifted downstream and pressed up against the keen edge of Gram's blade, the wool parted—as if by magic—and, thereafter, two smaller clumps continued on their journey to the fjord. Sigurd whistled in wonder, while Reginn smirked with self-satisfaction. Clearly Gram was one of the *sharpest* swords the Nine Worlds had ever seen.

"Now that you have your horse and your sword, Sigurd, it is time to face Fafnir!"

"Not so fast, Reginn. What kind of Volsung would I be if I went questing for gold while Sigmund's killer still lived? Once I have avenged my father, I will slay your dragon for you. That I promise."

Reginn gnashed his teeth but said nothing—for he needed Sigurd's help and feared to anger the young man.

Thus it was that Sigurd went before King Hjalprek and Prince Alf, told them of his plans to avenge Sigmund's death, and begged for the loan of a troop of warriors to assist him. Proud they were of Hjordis's son, for he was strong and handsome beyond other men—and his desire to avenge his father was a clear sign of his noble nature. Hjalprek and Alf gave Sigurd the pick of their finest warriors; Hjordis gave her son her blessings and a parting hug, and he and his new war band descended upon the lands of King Lyngvi, Sigmund's slayer, with fire and sword.

In the battles that followed—despite his youth—Sigurd proved to be the finest warrior the Northern lands had ever seen. Astride his mighty war horse and wielding his father's reforged sword, Sigurd was an irresistible force that cut through the army of his enemies like a hot knife cleaves a lump of butter. In the end, he slew King Lyngvi and his kinsmen, shattered their army, and—with his warband—returned in triumph to his mother and the court of Hjalprek and Alf.

When the excitement died down and Sigurd and Reginn finally had a chance to talk alone together, the smith demanded impatiently: "Well, your father is avenged and you have covered yourself with glory . . . now, is there any other reason why we cannot hunt down my brother, Fafnir?"

"None at all, Reginn. My horse is battle-tested, my blade is battle-tested, and I am battle-tested. Now, perhaps, we are up to the task. We can go whenever you wish."

Episode Three: Sigurd Meets the Dragon

So Sigurd and Reginn gathered their gear and provisions for the journey, and that night, when everyone else was asleep, they slipped quietly away. A full moon cast enough light that they were able to travel in the dark. Morning found them high in the mountains, at the edge of Gnita Heath where Fafnir—in dragon form—had his lair. Before long, Sigurd and Reginn came upon a broad earthen trail, the path gouged out of the living earth by the dragon's body when Fafnir crawled to and from a dark tarn to quench his thirst each day at dawn.

"He is no mere bog-orm, this brother of yours, Reginn. I had no idea a dragon could be so large."

"If he were a small dragon, Sigurd, some other bold fellow would have done for him ages ago. Be of stout heart, trust my advice, and all will be well."

"Oh, I am not fearful of Fafnir, just surprised at his size—that's all."

"That's my brave lad. But even you would have no chance against Fafnir face to face, so what you must do is dig a pit on the trail and hide in it. Then, when he crawls over it tomorrow on his way to the tarn, you can stab him from underneath where his armor is thinnest."

Sigurd agreed that this was a good plan and set about digging a pit with his sword. Meanwhile, Reginn went some distance away and settled down for a nap. Morning passed into afternoon, and Sigurd thought he was about finished with his task, when an old, one-eyed man came by and asked what he was doing. When Sigurd explained, the old man shook his head.

"This will never do, my boy. The dragon's blood will fill your pit and you will drown. Look you! Your pit is at a point where the trail begins to slope down toward the tarn. Dig some more pits farther down the trail and connect them to this one with a trench. Then, when the dragon's blood starts to flow, it will drain down to the lower pits—and you will be safe."

Sigurd did as the old man had suggested but, by the time he had finished, it was dark and he was so tired that he could scarcely eat more than a few bites of the supper Reginn had prepared before falling asleep where he sat.

The next thing Sigurd knew, Reginn was shaking his shoulder and saying urgently: "It's dawn, boy, and Fafnir is beginning to stir. You've got to hide in the pit at once. If he sees you, our plan will be ruined."

Sigurd took his sword Gram and dropped into the upper pit where he crouched, waiting. The shaking of the earth around him and an increasingly loud hissing sound announced Fafnir's approach. Suddenly, the light at the top of the pit was blotted out as the dragon crawled over the opening. Sigurd gripped the hilt of his sword firmly in both hands, then—when he reckoned the dragon's heart was passing above him—he thrust Gram upward with all his might. The keen blade passed through Fafnir's belly plates almost as easily as it had the clump of wool. The mortally wounded dragon let out a bellow of pain and rage, and began to thrash wildly about—all the while spraying his surroundings with sheets of venom, the dreaded "cold fire" of dragonkind.

A blood-drenched Sigurd scrambled up out of the pit, his sword half-raised to strike another blow if one were needed. But it was not—and the dying dragon and his human slayer looked upon each other for the first time.

"Who are you?" rumbled Fafnir. "Who was your father, and who were your kinsmen? You must come from bold stock, indeed, that you dared to raise a weapon against me."

Now it was well known that it is unwise to reveal your true name to a dying enemy lest he put a curse upon you, so Sigurd replied: "I am called Stag, a homeless wanderer with no parents and no kinsmen."

"What wonder is this? If you had no parents, then how were you born? I may be dying, but we both know that you are lying to me."

Ashamed that his fear had momentarily replaced his honor, Sigurd said: "I am of the Volsung clan, that famed and noble lineage. It is Sigurd Sigmundson you see before you. Now you know whose sword has given you your death blow."

"I see," mused Fafnir. "Still I think you did not take up this deed on your own. Who talked you into it . . . and why did you let yourself be persuaded? Had you not heard how everyone fears me? You must have had a bold father, indeed, to undertake such a task."

"'Twas my own bold spirit spurred me to this deed," retorted Sigurd. "And my own strong arm and sharp sword helped me in its doing. He who is not bold in youth is scarce likely to become so when he grows older."

"If you had grown up among your famed kinsmen, I would not be so surprised at what you have done. But it is a great wonder that one who is not his own master would dare to face me—seldom are thralls bold in battle."

"Scoff at me if you will, old orm, but it was no thrall's blade that skewered you. Honored am I in Hjalprek's court, and Prince Alf is my stepfather."

"Oh, prickly are we? It matters little. But this I tell you in truth: take my golden hoard and it will be the death of you."

"Death comes to every man sooner or later, but not every man can gain great wealth," replied Sigurd.

"Heed my advice, boy. Take your horse and ride away as fast and as far as you can lest the curse fall upon you."

"I hear your counsel, Fafnir, but I choose to follow my own will. When you are dead, I will ride to your lair and fetch away all your gold."

"Then you shall find more than enough gold to satisfy your needs for all your days—but there won't be many of them. Reginn has betrayed me, and he'll betray you, too. That gold will be the doom of both of us." The dragon began to cough blood and his voice grew weaker.

"My death is upon me now . . . but I see yours looming in the mist." And with that, Fafnir shuddered once and lay still.

Sigurd stood silently for a time, gazing upon the body of the great dragon, then turned away from the corpse and began to clean the blood from his sword blade upon the grass. Just then Reginn came up, for he had been watching from afar off—where he would have been safe had Sigurd failed and Fafnir been the victor.

"Well done, my boy, you have slain Fafnir and won the day. Surely, of all men you are the bravest."

Sigurd replied, modestly: "As for that, who is to say? Many a man is brave who has yet to redden his sword in a foeman's chest. Such things can only be decided on the field of battle."

"Be that as it may, Sigurd, it is you who has triumphed here—and 'tis a deed that will be remembered in the North so long as skalds tongues to tell of it. Still, if truth be told, it is my brother that you slew . . . and I had a hand in it."

"You were hiding in the rocks while I did this deed, Reginn. It was my strength and sword that took the dragon's life, so you will gain neither blame nor credit for it."

"Long had Fafnir dwelt upon Gnita Heath, Sigurd. Had you not had the aid of that sharp sword, which I made for you with these hands of mine, he might well be living there for ages more to come."

"Courage is better than cold steel when bold deeds are to be done. Often have I seen a stout-hearted warrior prevail with a dull blade, while a better-armed but fearful man gave way. Still," Sigurd admitted, "'twas your advice that I ride into the high mountains on this quest; save for your urging, Fafnir would still have both his life and his hoard."

Reginn seemed somewhat appeased by Sigurd's admission and, taking his own sword, Reginn cut out Fafnir's heart. He gulped a mouthful of blood that dripped from the gory organ, then held it out to Sigurd: "After all this excitement, I would nap and dream a bit. Take this tasty morsel and roast it for me, if you will, for I intend to eat it when I wake."

So Sigurd built a campfire, skewered the dragon heart on a spit, and began to roast it over the flames. After a time, the heart began to hiss and bubble, and Sigurd wondered if the meat was done. So he gingerly touched it with one finger, which, of course, promptly got burnt.

"Oww, that hurts," Sigurd muttered, and he did what anyone else would have done—he stuck the injured finger in his mouth and sucked on it. In so doing, he tasted the dragon's blood, and changed his world forever. For, as you surely know, dragons are magical creatures and their blood contains the very essence of the runes; even to taste it begins to unlock the secrets of nature. Sigurd's hearing seemed to become keener, and—to his amazement—he could actually understand the conversation of three willow tits that were cavorting in the branches of a nearby tree.

"Tew-tew-tew, there sits foolish Sigurd roasting the dragon's heart for Reginn. He should be eating it himself so he can become wiser than other men," said the first bird.

"Yes, and there sleeps Reginn, who would betray the one who trusts him," replied the second, wisely cocking his little black cap.

"Sigurd should hew off his head and send Reginn down the Hel Way," chattered the third. "Then Sigurd alone will be lord of Fafnir's golden hoard."

The first bird hung upside down beneath his branch. "Well advised would Sigurd be to harken to our words, look to his own interests, and feed Reginn to the ravens—for where a wolf's ears peep out, there lies a wolf in waiting."

"Tew-tew, tew-true," replied the second tit. "Sigurd is less wise than I think if he lets live a man whose brother he has slain—Reginn has lied to him and even now plots vengeance for his kinsman."

"Enough," growled Sigurd. "It is not fated that Reginn shall be my bane—it is better that both brothers tread the Hel Way this day." And, having said this, Sigurd unsheathed Gram and lopped off Reginn's head. Then, while eating the dragon's heart, Sigurd heard the willow tits addressing him directly—for now they knew that he could understand them.

"Tew-tew-tew, Sigurd. Well done, hero. Go now to Fafnir's cave and gather his golden hoard. Then wend your way to Hindarfjell, where more wonders await you. A high golden hall sits upon the mountain crest, surrounded by a wall of flame. Within a maiden sleeps a magical sleep. If you are but bold enough to dare the flames—and wise enough to wake the maid—then may you win her gifts of love and lore."

So Sigurd rode Grani back up the dragon's path to its cave, and there found so much treasure that he filled two great chests with it. On his finger he placed a golden ring that happened to catch his fancy; then he strapped the chests across Grani's flanks and tied the Helm of Terror, a golden chainmail shirt, and Fafnir's sword atop the chests. Sigurd thought to walk alongside Grani to spare him more weight, but the gray was so strong and so proud that he would not budge until Sigurd mounted into the saddle. That being done, the horse and his master slowly traveled southward toward Hindarfjell.

Episode Four: Sigurd Awakens Brynhild

Sigurd and Grani rode for many a long day before finally beginning to ascend the slopes of Hindarfjell. As they drew nearer to their goal, Sigurd noticed a glow on the horizon that grew ever brighter. At last they arrived at the very top of the treeless mountain, and there discovered a circular wall of fire. Grani did not shy away from the fearsome flames but stood quietly, awaiting his master's command. As for Sigurd, he viewed the fiery wall with awe but his heart knew no fear.

"Well, Grani, we've come too far seeking the magic maiden to be stopped by any barrier, even one such as this. So, brave heart, let us attempt to leap the wall of fire—and together we shall triumph . . . or perish, if that be the Norns' decree."

The big gray pawed the ground impatiently, then hurled himself forward at a gallop. At the last possible instant, Grani leapt as high as his powerful hind legs would carry him, and he and his rider cleared the flames without so much as a singed hair.

Once past the fiery barrier, Sigurd found himself facing a stately hall, walled about with shields of gold. Dismounting, and leaving Grani free to graze on the rich mountain grass, Sigurd stepped through a gap in the shield wall and entered the hall. There, at its center, he beheld a bed . . . and on it lay the body of a warrior, helmeted and covered from neck to knee in a war shirt of chain mail.

"What is this?" thought Sigurd, angrily. "The birds said I would find a magic maiden on Hindarfjell, and all I see here is a man." Sigurd pulled the helmet from the warrior's head . . . and his anger turned to awe as he beheld the tumbling golden curls of the most beautiful woman he had ever set eyes upon. But was she dead or only sleeping?

The chain mail shirt seemed to fit as tightly as a second skin, and Sigurd wondered if it might be keeping the woman from breathing properly. Perhaps it was not too late to save her! Hurriedly he drew Gram from its sheath and carefully slit the chain mail from neck to knee, then out along each arm, and the metal shirt slid away from her body like the retreating sea at low tide.

The woman's bosom quivered, then began to rise and fall rhythmically, and soon her eyes fluttered open. She sighed deeply: "What cut away my chain mail shirt? Who freed me from my dreamless sleep?"

Their eyes met, and through them their two souls flowed—each into the other. Sigurd knelt down, took her hands into his, and replied: "'Tis Sigurd Sigmundson who kneels beside you, lady, and it is his sword Gram, Fafnir's Bane, that has freed you from your dreamless sleep. But tell me, fairest one, what is your name and how did you come to be here?"

"I am called Brynhild Budlisdottir," she said softly as she let Sigurd draw her into a sitting position. "And I grew up in Hlymdal, the home of Heimir, my sister's husband. I was a headstrong maid and often galloped about the livelong day following my own will. Then one day Odin came upon me in my wanderings and called me to become one of his Valkyries. Craving excitement, I followed him to Asgard—though, if truth be told, I don't know if Odin really would have given me any choice in the matter. All-Father doesn't like to have his will thwarted—as I was to discover.

"It was a thrilling life and I was happy for a time—riding off to battle, causing one hero to win and another to lose, and carrying the loser off to Valhalla to join the ranks of Odin's army of the dead. And when there were no wars going on, my sister Valkyries and I would don our swan cloaks and fly away to far-off lands. It was so exciting! Then, one day, Odin decreed that I should help Helmet-Gunnar slay young Agnar. But Helmet-Gunnar was old and ugly, and Agnar such a handsome young man that I just couldn't do it. So, when they were whaling away at each other with their swords, I just happened to snatch off Gunnar's helmet . . . and it wasn't very long before Agnar's sword cleaved Gunnar's skull right down to his chin.

"Well, Odin was furious that I had disobeyed him. He declared that I was unfit to be a Valkyrie and brought me here to Hindarfjell. Odin said he was going to prick me with a sleep-thorn and I would have to wed whoever awakened me—old or young, handsome or ugly, man or troll. I was frightened, of course, but feeling I had no more to lose, I defiantly declared that if marry I must, it would only be to a man who knew no fear.

"Odin chuckled at that—I think he admires a woman with spirit—and he cast a wall of flames around this hall. 'Be it as you wish, Brynhild. No fearful man shall ever dare to pass this wall.' Then he pricked me in the neck with a sleep-thorn and I remember nothing more until now . . . though I have the strangest feeling that he may have gently kissed my brow just as I dropped off to sleep." Brynhild paused. "But enough about me; tell me more of yourself."

The maid sat in rapt fascination as Sigurd related his finding of Grani, the reforging of his father's broken sword, his avenging of Sigmund's death, his slaying of the dragon, his dispatch of the treacherous Reginn, and his freeing of Brynhild. "The birds never said that you were a Valkyrie, but they did tell me that you are a wise woman. Despite all that I have done, I am still quite young . . . and there is so much that I would learn from you of love and lore—if you are willing to teach me."

"With all my heart," Brynhild replied, "for you are all that I could have dreamed of in a mate, and willingly will I give you my love and share my lore. But I must warn you, Sigurd, that both are perilous. To marry a Valkyrie is to court early death, and the lore I can teach you is the lore of the runes. With that knowledge you will know more of earth and stars, gods and giants, slaying and healing, life and death than any man before you . . . and you will know your own doom. Do you still wish to love and learn from me, Sigurd? The choice is yours."

"A wiser and more lovely woman than you does not live in this world, Brynhild, and I vow that you shall be my wife, for you are all that I desire."

"And you would I have for my husband, Sigurd, though I had my choice among all men."

The lovers embraced and let touch express the feelings that words could not.

Sitting side by side or lying in each other's arms, the days and nights passed quickly as Sigurd learned the lessons of love and the secrets of the runes from his lovely teacher. The whole world seemed to grow larger as his eyes were opened to all that lay around—and within—him. But knowledge, untempered by the wisdom that age may bring, can prove to be a fickle and dangerous power, and Sigurd slowly grew more and more eager to experience the world about which he was learning so much.

Thus it was that one morning Sigurd declared that Brynhild deserved nothing less than the Northland's greatest hero as her husband . . . and he would not be worthy of that title or of her until he had accomplished more great deeds. In vain, Brynhild tried to convince him that slaying Fafnir and winning the dragon's golden hoard was a greater deed than any other hero had ever achieved. But Sigurd was adamant that he needed to do far more—slay a wicked wizard or a giant, perhaps, and certainly win a kingdom or two. After all, for now he had no kingdom of his own where he could take her and make her his queen.

Brynhild would have been quite content to be queen of their little kingdom of two atop Hindarfjell, but she also was wise enough not to thwart Sigurd's wishes when she could see his mind was made up. There were no tethers on her human falcon, and if their love was strong enough—he would return.

Since she was no longer a Valkyrie, it was clear that Brynhild could not accompany Sigurd into battle, so he took her as far as Hlymdal at the foot of Hindarfjell, where she was sure she could live with her sister until Sigurd returned. When they parted company outside her sister's hall, Sigurd slipped the ring Andvaranaut from his finger and placed it on hers, vowing his undying love and pledging to return for her once he had won a kingdom for them. He did not know, of course, that the ring was cursed or he would have cut off his own finger before passing the ring and the curse on to his beloved. So Sigurd rode off to seek a kingdom, while Brynhild remained in Hlymdal—to wait, hope, and learn patience.

Episode Five: The Curse Strikes Again

Before traveling very many days, Sigurd and Grani rode up to the hall of Gjuki, a powerful ruler in those parts. When the king and his queen, Grimhild, learned that their visitor was the son of the famous King Sigmund, they greeted him warmly and invited him to stay with them as long as he liked—and he readily accepted. Gjuki and Grimhild had a daughter, Gudrun, and three sons: Gunnar, Hogni, and Guttorm. The two older brothers were of an age with Sigurd, and they all enjoyed spending time together: hunting, hawking, fencing, and shooting the bow. And at all of these sports, Sigurd excelled. He reveled in the companionship of Gunnar and Hogni, and he enjoyed the praise heaped upon him by the king and queen. Grimhild, in particular, had a way of drawing him out . . . and before long he had told her all about slaying Fafnir, taking the dragon's gold, and his love for Brynhild.

Now Grimhild, though beautiful, was really quite wicked—and she decided that a rich young hero of Sigurd's stature would make an excellent son-in-law, his love for Brynhild being but a minor obstacle. So Grimhild brewed a magic potion, and one evening she added it to the ale in Sigurd's drinking horn. Alas, the moment he swallowed the tainted brew he completely forgot that Brynhild even existed.

Thereafter, the queen made sure that Sigurd was thrown often into the company of her daughter, Gudrun. The princess was quite pretty and wise, so it wasn't long before Sigurd was seeking her out himself. Grimhild hugged herself with joy, for her plan was working out just as she had wished. One evening, when Sigurd was outside admiring the sunset with Gudrun, Grimhild suggested to Gjuki, Gunnar, and Hogni that they should give Gudrun to Sigurd in marriage.

The men all thought this to be a wonderful idea for they liked and admired Sigurd and had dreaded the moment when he might decide to leave. Married to Gudrun and given a part of the kingdom, he would stay with them forever. When this proposition was presented to Sigurd, he was quick to agree for he was quite smitten by the lovely princess . . . and she had come to fall deeply in love with him, too. Gunnar and Hogni were so delighted that they swore oaths of blood-brotherhood with Sigurd, but young Guttorm was not considered old enough to swear an oath.

The wedding feast lasted for days and was the finest the kingdom had ever seen. In the months that followed, Sigurd and Gudrun had great joy of each other. Moreover, he and his blood-brothers rode against Gjuki's enemies, overthrowing them all, and bringing home much treasure.

In time, Gudrun gave birth to a son, whom they called Sigmund (after his grandfather), and Sigurd knew great bliss. But it was not to last . . . for the curse would have its way.

One day, Grimhild went to Gunnar and told him: "You know, my son, it is high time that you produced an heir, so the Gjuking line might continue unbroken."

"That is all well and good, mother, but I have no wife—as well you know."

Grimhild replied: "If you will take my advice, you will seek the hand of Brynhild Budlisdottir. They say she is a beautiful young woman, and I know that her father is quite wealthy." Then she added maliciously: "Why don't you take Sigurd along with you when you go courting. I'm sure he would be good company."

Gunnar agreed to his mother's plan, and soon thereafter he and Sigurd rode off to Budli's kingdom. Budli thought Gunnar to be a suitable suitor for Brynhild and he gave the marriage his blessing—so long as his daughter was agreeable. When Gunnar asked to speak to her, Budli told him he would have to seek Brynhild in Hlymdal where she lived with his other daughter, the wife of Heimir.

So Gunnar and Sigurd rode to Hlymdal, but once there they were told by Heimir that while his sister-in-law had been living in his hall for several years awaiting the return of her wandering lover, recently she had reluctantly decided he was never coming back. Downhearted and thoroughly distrustful of the promises of men, she had retreated to her hall high on Hindarfjell and vowed she would never wed, save for that man who would brave the wall of flames surrounding her hall.

Gunnar was intrigued by the story, and before long he and Sigurd were riding up Hindarfjell to press his suit. But when Gunnar tried to ride through the flames, his horse balked and would not go forward. Gunnar asked Sigurd for the loan of Grani, and Sigurd was willing—but Grani would accept no rider but his master. So Sigurd offered to change shapes with his blood-brother, an illusion Grimhild had taught him, and to court Brynhild for him. Gunnar could see no other choice, so Sigurd and Grani braved the flames again—although Sigurd had no memory of having done so before.

When Sigurd entered the hall, Brynhild was startled—for she had thought only Sigurd could pass the flames, and this man was unknown to her.

"Who are you, stranger, who enters my hall unbidden?"

"I am Gunnar Gjukison," replied Sigurd, "and I have come to seek you for my wife. Your father has given his consent, should you be willing. I am told you promised to marry whomever could ride through the wall of fire, and—as you can see—I have done so."

"I scarcely know what to say, Gunnar, for in truth I was expecting someone else."

"His loss, my lady. Having seen you I could not bear to step aside for someone else . . . and a vow is a vow."

Brynhild bowed her head in defeat, and agreed to Gunnar's proposal. That night she and Sigurd (in the guise of Gunnar) slept in the same bed, but before he lay down Sigurd drew his sword Gram and placed the naked blade between them. Brynhild thought this peculiar, but Sigurd assured her it was part of an oath he had sworn and one he must keep.

The next morning, after exchanging rings and agreeing to hold the wedding in Gjuki's hall in a fortnight, Sigurd rode off to tell Gunnar of his success, while Brynhild returned to Hlymdal to make her wedding arrangements. One of those arrangements was to leave her little daughter, Aslaug, of whom Sigurd—the child's father—knew nothing, to be raised by Brynhild's sister and her husband.

At the wedding feast, Brynhild was shocked to see Sigurd there with Gudrun—and then she was horrified that he acted as if he did not recognize her, she whom he had sworn was his heart and soul. Deeply hurt, she resolved that two could play at that game.

A shock was awaiting Sigurd, too, for the nasty mind of Grimhild couldn't resist stirring up unhappiness. When Sigurd wasn't looking, she switched his ale for a magical drink that wiped away the effects of the potion of forgetfulness she had given him shortly after he had first come to Gjuki's hall. With the first swallow, Sigurd recognized Brynhild for who she was and remembered all that she had meant to him. But heartsick as he was, Sigurd knew that he could not bear to hurt his wife, Gudrun, or his blood-brother, Gunnar, for he loved them, too. So Sigurd remained silent and, in the days that followed, he treated Brynhild only as one would treat an honored sister-in-law. Believing that nothing could be done to change things, and since Brynhild never demanded an explanation, Sigurd never told her why he hadn't returned for her. Lacking the explanation she was too proud to demand, Brynhild, of course, believed him to be faithless and uncaring—and her love turned to bitterness.

One day, when Brynhild and Gudrun went down to the river to bathe, the curse of Andvaranaut began to move more rapidly toward its conclusion. Brynhild waded a bit upstream from Gudrun, who asked her sister-in-law why she did this.

"Why should I, who have the greater husband, bathe downstream from your filth?" replied Brynhild, haughtily. "Gunnar is a noble prince and braved the wall of fire to win me, while your husband is only a vassal of King Hjalprek."

"That is ill and spitefully said," retorted Gudrun angrily. "My Sigurd is the bravest of all heroes, for he slew the dragon Fafnir. What's more, it was he and not my brother who rode through the flames to woo you in Gunnar's guise."

"You lie!" hissed Brynhild, red-faced.

"Oh, do I? Then how do you explain my having the ring he took from you when you thought you were exchanging vows with my brother on Hindarfjell?" For Sigurd, acting on what he thought was a whim, had given Andvaranaut to Gudrun as a keepsake rather than passing it on to Gunnar.

When Brynhild saw the ring in Gudrun's possession, she could only believe that Sigurd had done it to mock her, and her bitterness turned to hatred. White-faced and shaking with rage, Brynhild waded out of the stream, donned her garments, walked slowly back to Gunnar's hall, and went straight to her bed.

When Brynhild failed to appear for supper that evening, Gunnar went to her to see if she was ill. At first she would not speak to him and pulled away from his touch, but at last she icily told him that she had learned from Gudrun the truth of their courtship. Reluctantly, Gunnar admitted that the story was true, but he declared that he loved her dearly and it wasn't his fault that neither horse would carry him through the flames.

"Well, Gunnar, if you want to win back my love, you are going to have to kill Sigurd for me. I hate him as I have hated no other man."

"Be reasonable, sweetling," protested Gunnar. "He's my blood-brother and has always behaved honorably toward me."

"How noble of him was it to sleep with your wife on Hindarfjell?" By now, Brynhild was so filled with hatred that she deliberately failed to tell Gunnar about the naked sword Sigurd had placed between them.

Stunned and outraged by what he thought was Sigurd's betrayal, Gunnar agreed to her demand for Sigurd's death, and he went to see his brother Hogni about helping him. Hogni distrusted Brynhild's motives and was opposed to killing Sigurd.

"By Odin's silvery beard, Gunnar, he *is* our blood-brother. If we break our oaths by slaying our kinsman, no good will come of it. You mark my words."

"But our younger brother, Guttorm, never swore an oath, Hogni. Let's persuade him to do the deed."

Hogni still didn't like the idea, but Gunnar finally got him to reluctantly agree. Guttorm had long been jealous of Sigurd's popularity—especially with his older brothers—so he was only too willing to do the deed.

Early the next morning, Guttorm crept into the bedroom where Sigurd and Gudrun lay sleeping and drove his sword into Sigurd's chest with such force that it went through the mattress and into the bed frame. Then, overcome with the enormity of his deed, Guttorm fled. But before he could escape, the mortally wounded Sigurd drew Gram from its sheath one last time and hurled the sword at the fleeing Guttorm. So powerful was Sigurd's throw that Guttorm was sliced in half and died on the spot.

With his dying words, Sigurd assured Gudrun of his love but also told her the whole story of his earlier love for Brynhild, as well as Grimhild's wickedness and what had come of it. Then he asked her to look after their young son, and with that he died.

Gudrun went to Brynhild and told her what Sigurd had revealed on his death bed. When the gloating Brynhild heard about Grimhild's treachery she turned ashen.

"Oh, Sigurd, my love! What have I done, what *have* I done!" Then Brynhild snatched up a sword and, falling upon it, gave herself a mortal wound. With her last words she made Gunnar promise to lay her body on Sigurd's funeral pyre so that their two spirits might be joined in the afterlife. As the rising flames consumed their earthly bodies, their spirits ascended to Valhalla to join the warrior dead, and the Ring of Doom passed into the hands of lesser beings.

PART FOUR: HAMMER AND MISTLETOE

These nine stories focus on the exploits of Thor, the enmity of the giants, and—ultimately—the destruction of the Nine Worlds. The transformation of Loki from a merely annoying mischief-maker to an almost demonic figure of evil underlies much of the concluding section of this book.

Thor's Visit to Utgard

Thor's confidence in his ability to overcome any giant is severely shaken when he and Loki visit Utgard and must pass a series of challenges.

Thor took it in his head one day to pay a visit to the giants' fabled castle of Utgard, deep in the forests of Jötunheim—not with his usual intention of killing giants, but simply to see the sights. This adventure appealed to Loki, too—when he learned of it—and he soon convinced Thor to take him along. So early one morning, the two of them hopped into Thor's goat cart and set off for Giant Home. They traveled all that day, and, just before dusk, Thor and Loki—tired and hungry—stopped at a small farmstead to seek lodging for the night.

The farmer, Egil by name, greeted them courteously and said they would be welcome to the bed he and his wife shared—the couple could sleep on skins by the fire—but he feared that he had no food that would be suitable fare for the gods.

"Don't worry about that," rumbled Thor. "Loki and I have simple tastes. But we don't wish to be a burden on your meager larder, so we'll provide the meat . . . fresh goat meat."

Sure enough, when Egil had gotten a good fire going and set a cauldron of water over it to boil, Thor took his hammer, Mjöllnir, and killed each of his two cart-pulling goats with a single blow to the head. Thwak! Thwak!

"There now, Egil. You may skin and cook the goats. Just be very, *very* sure that once the meal is over all the bones are gathered up in the skins."

The farmer hastened to assure Thor that all would be done as he had commanded, but unbeknownst to anyone, during the course of the meal Egil's son, Thjalfi, broke open one of the thigh bones to suck out the marrow.

The next morning when Thor arose and went outside, he held his hammer above the bundle of goathides and bones and muttered a runic charm. The goats were immediately restored to life, just as good as new—except that one goat was lame in a back leg. Thor was furious, and his eyes shot sparks.

"Egil, come out here . . . *at once!* Just look what someone in your family has done—broken my goat's leg, that's what. Now I can't use my cart for the rest of this trip. Give me one good reason why I shouldn't flatten this whole farmstead—and you and your family with it!"

Of course, Egil and his wife were terrified and, knees knocking, they begged the Thunder God for mercy. Well, despite having a short and violent temper, Thor was basically good-hearted. So he relented, but he did insist on taking Thjalfi and his sister, Roskva, along as his servants in compensation for the damage to his goat.

Since the goats could no longer pull the cart, Thor left them in Egil's care, and the four companions had to walk the rest of the way to Jötunheim. Shortly after crossing into Giant Home, they entered a forest so vast that they were still deep within it when darkness fell. In looking about for lodging, they chanced upon a rather strange-looking building with an entrance as wide as the hall, but without a door. The foursome cautiously went inside, but finding no one about, they curled up on the floor and soon fell asleep. About midnight, they were awakened by a violent shaking of the earth, and soon thereafter they heard a low, growling noise outside. Everyone but Thor was frightened, so they all went deeper into the hall and, finding a side room, they decided to sleep there after Thor agreed to sit in the opening to keep out intruders.

At first light, Thor went outside to see if he could find the source of the growling—and there he discovered a truly enormous giant, asleep and snoring! Annoyed about his own loss of sleep, Thor was about to strike him with his hammer, when the giant awoke and sat up. For once, Thor hesitated about killing a giant. Instead he asked: "What's your name, big fellow?"

"Why, I'm called Skrymir. But I don't need to ask who you are. You could only be the god Thor. By the way, have you seen a mitten anywhere? I lost one around here somewhere, but I couldn't find it in the dark. Oh, there it is behind you . . . and some people are coming out of it. Friends of yours, perhaps?"

Sure enough. Thor, Loki, and the two young humans had spent the night in the thumb of Skrymir's mitten—which gives you some idea just how big that giant really was.

Skrymir asked if he could accompany them, then offered to carry all their provisions in his pack. Unfortunately, Skrymir walked with such great strides that he soon outdistanced the others and it was only when he stopped for the night that they finally caught up with him. Skrymir was lying beneath a great oak tree, yawning.

"Hyaah," echoed from his cavernous mouth. "I thought you'd *never* get here. I've already eaten and am going to sleep now. You're welcome to get your provisions out of my pack. Just untie the knot. See you in the morning." And soon Skrymir was snoring lustily.

Thor struggled and struggled to undo the knot on Skrymir's pack, but finally he had to admit defeat. This so frustrated Thor that he decided to bash Skrymir with his hammer—muttering that that's what he should have done in the first place. And Thor let the deed follow the thought. But, much to the Thunder God's surprise, Skrymir's skull did not crack under the force of that mighty blow.

"You still up, Thor? A leaf must have fallen on my head and wakened me. Well, we'd both better get some sleep. It will be a long day tomorrow."

Thor just glowered, but waited a long time—until he was sure that Skrymir was sound asleep—before trying again to kill the giant. Thor reared back and struck such a mighty blow that the head of the hammer disappeared into Skrymir's skull. Imagine Thor's dismay when the giant rolled over and looked around.

"Why, you're awake, too, Thor. Did you also get hit by an acorn? I guess it wasn't too smart of us to camp under an oak tree, was it?" And Skrymir promptly went back to sleep.

Just before dawn, the Thunder God—who was beginning to question his own fabled strength (not to mention that of his hammer)—tried a third time to smash Skrymir's skull. Never had Thor swung Mjöllnir any harder, but all that happened was that Skrymir sat up, stretched, and got to his feet.

"I see it's almost dawn. That's why the birds are getting restless, and why one of them pooped on me. Well, it's time for us to get up and get going, too. Here is where we part company. My path lies to the north, but if you intend to visit Utgard, you'll need to turn to the east. Even as slowly as you little folks walk, you should reach Utgard by mid-day. By the way, let me give you some advice. You'll meet some really powerful giants there, so it wouldn't be wise to be too boastful about your accomplishments. Fare thee well, Thor."

With that, Skrymir hoisted his pack on his back and plowed off through the forest. He had neglected to give Thor and his companions their own provisions, so they were extremely hungry by the time they emerged from the forest and saw a huge castle sitting in the middle of a wide plain.

The company walked on until they reached the castle gates, which were closed. At first they thought they wouldn't be able to get inside, but the gates proved to be so large that they were able to turn sideways and slip through a crack between two planks. Once within the gates, they came to a great hall with its door standing wide open. Entering, Thor and his friends cautiously trod the length of the hall between two rows of seated giants, who silently peered at the uninvited visitors. At last the party from Asgard arrived at the foot of the high seat of the giants' king, Utgard-Loki himself.

"Who are you people, and why do you come into my hall so boldly? Why, can this red-bearded pipsqueak be the god Thor we've heard so much about? Hmph, well maybe there's more to you than meets the eye. There had better be, for no one is allowed to remain in Utgard who is not skilled at something."

Thor was so insulted by the king's demeaning remarks that he was at a loss for words. Loki, however, was quick to respond.

"I can't speak for Thor, oh king, but I can eat food faster than anyone—and right now I'm nearly starved."

"A fast eater, eh? All right, let's see how you fare against Logi, our champion. Your names sound enough alike that it will be almost like competing against yourself—or me." And Utgard-Loki smiled menacingly.

Two wooden troughs filled with roasted meat were set end to end. Loki was stationed at one end, Logi at the other. Whoever reached the middle first was to be declared the winner. Loki ate with the speed of an ocean gale and, hungry as he was, he soon reached the stopping point. Looking up, he saw that Logi had finished at just the same time, so the Trickster thought he had done no worse than gain a tie. His eyes grew wide, however, when he saw that his opponent had consumed not only the meat, but the bones and wooden trough as well!

Then Thjalfi spoke up: "I-I'm said to be a fast runner."

"Oh, really?" responded the king. "Well, let's go outside and see how you compare with young Hugi there."

They all walked out onto the plain surrounding Utgard, and the king pointed to the nearest patch of woods. "First one to the woods and back is the winner," and at Utgard-Loki's signal the runners sped off. Thjalfi ran as if Fenris Wolf were breathing down his neck, but by the time he returned to the castle gates, Hugi was already there waiting to greet him. The king allowed Thjalfi a second chance, but this time Hugi beat him by a bowshot. The nearly exhausted boy pleaded for one last chance, which Utgard-Loki granted, but Thjalfi's legs had lost their spring, and he had not even reached the woods before Hugi had completed the race.

"Still," conceded the giant king, "you ran remarkably well—for a human. Now, Thor, it seems to me that it's high time you showed us what you can do."

"Well," snarled Thor, "I can drink any giant in Utgard under the table."

"Oh, fancy yourself a great drinker, do you? Let's just go back into my hall and give you a chance to prove it."

When the group was once more assembled before Utgard-Loki's high seat, the king handed Thor a huge drinking horn. The mouth was not unusually wide, but just where the horn ended was anything but clear to the Thunder God.

"Well, Thor, let's see if you can live up to your boast. Only the best drinkers among us giants can empty this horn in a single swallow, but most can do so in two . . . and no giant is so feeble as to fail to empty it in three."

Thor lifted the horn to his lips and took a mighty swallow. But when he stopped for breath and looked into the horn, he could scarcely see that the level had gone down at all.

"What are you holding back for, Thor? Surely you can empty the horn this time."

Thor took a deep breath and tried again. This time he could see a little progress—but not much. Utgard-Loki just shook his head and uttered a loud "tsk-tsk."

The third time, Thor breathed as deeply as he possibly could and swallowed until he turned purple, but still he failed to empty the horn.

"Hmph, well, so much for drinking. I heard that you are supposed to be quite strong. Do you think you could lift my cat off the floor?" And the giant king pointed to a large gray cat sleeping near the fire.

"That shouldn't be very difficult," said Thor, though with less confidence than he had had before his failure with the drinking horn.

The Thunder God knelt down, placed one hand beneath the cat's belly, and lifted. And he kept on lifting until he was standing on tiptoes with his arm fully extended—but the cat just kept arching its back, so the most Thor could do before he ran out of reach was to force one of the cat's feet free of the floor.

"Phew, this is really embarrassing. I could have sworn I'd be able to lift that cat. I know I'm stronger than that. Give me one more chance to prove myself, Utgard-Loki, just one more chance."

"What! Is the mighty Thor becoming humble? Will wonders never cease. And just what is it that you think you *can* do, Thunder God?"

Infuriated by his own humiliating failures and the giant-king's goading, Thor snarled: "I can outwrestle any giant in the hall."

"Hmm. After what we've seen so far, I can't imagine how any of our giants would gain any honor from throwing such a weak little fellow. Still, I *would* like to give you a final chance. I know, I'll let you wrestle my old nursemaid, Elli. Maybe she's more your speed."

It says a great deal about the state of Thor's morale that he made no objection, but suffered the insult in silence as he turned to face the gnarled old giantess who hobbled toward him, cackling. They locked hands, and each strove to force the other to the floor. Thor had no luck whatsoever in moving Elli so much as an inch, and soon he felt himself weakening. The Thunder God struggled mightily to stay on his feet; however, slowly but surely he was forced to one knee, and at that point Utgard-Loki declared the contest over.

"You've had your chances but haven't excelled at anything—so you cannot remain in Utgard. Still, lest anyone accuse me of being a poor host, you are welcome to stay the night and leave first thing in the morning."

Thor and his companions accepted the king's invitation, though it is not surprising that they did not feel very merry at the feast that night. Utgard-Loki came to them at dawn, had breakfast with the party, and escorted them beyond the gates of Utgard.

"Well, Thor, tell me truthfully. Did your visit to Jötunheim and Utgard go as you had expected? Did you meet anyone mightier than yourself?"

"The truth be told, I'm really rather ashamed of how I fared in your contests . . . and, for that matter, in my encounter with a giant called Skrymir we met in the woods on our way to Utgard. I dread the thought of you and the other giants calling me a weakling."

The Thunder God looked so miserable that Utgard-Loki took pity on him.

"Now that you are safely outside Utgard, I am going to tell you what really has been happening the past two days. Had I known beforehand how powerful you are, I would never have allowed you to enter Utgard in the first place. All of your apparent failures were due to my illusions.

"First of all, know that *I* was Skrymir. The pack you couldn't open to get your provisions was fastened up by an iron binding—not a knotted thong, as you thought. As for your failure to kill me with your hammer . . . " The giant king paused and Thor looked rather sheepish. "Do you see that mountain in the distance with the three deep valleys in its side? You made each of those valleys with one blow when I magically slipped the mountain between my head and your hammer.

"As for the contests here in Utgard . . . they, too, were not what they seemed to be. Loki's eating opponent was not a giant, but 'Wildfire,' which is what the name Logi means in our language. Is it any wonder that the bones and trough were consumed in his flame?

"Your servant Thjalfi is very fleet of foot—I have seen no human run faster—but my runner, Hugi, was my thoughts, and what man can outrun 'Thought'?

"When you drank from my horn, Thor, you didn't realize that the other end of it was in the ocean. If you should pass by the sea shore, you'll be able to see for yourself what a mighty draught you swallowed. Henceforth, folk will call it the ebb tide.

"My cat, as you may have guessed by now, was no cat at all. No, indeed, it was really Jörmungand, the dreaded Midgard Serpent. All of us were filled with terror when you succeeded in lifting one of his feet off the floor—we feared you were about to pull him completely out of the ocean depths and drag the great sea-dragon right into my hall." The giant king shuddered at the thought.

"Finally, Thor, there was no shame in failing to outwrestle Elli, for in reality she is 'Old Age,' and sooner or later she brings everyone to his knees.

"Now let us part company, and I think it would be better for both of us if you never seek me or Utgard again. Now that I know your strength, I'll use all the magic at my command to protect me and mine. Fare you well, son of Odin."

Thor turned red with rage at the thought of the tricks that had been played on him, and he raised his hammer to strike Utgard-Loki a blow . . . but the giant king had disappeared. Thwarted, Thor turned toward the castle, intending to smash it into rubble, but—lo and behold—Utgard, too, had vanished, and the companions were left standing dumbfounded on a vast empty plain.

So Thor learned to respect the magical powers of at least one giant, but the humiliation he had suffered only deepened his hatred for the whole race. The Thunder God also vowed to seek out the Midgard Serpent, and he pledged that his next encounter with that monster would have a different ending.

Thor Goes Fishing

Thor and Tyr visit the giant Hymir to win a huge cauldron for brewing ale. Thor also re-encounters his nemesis, the Midgard Serpent.

Now it happened that the Aesir gods had gathered a huge quantity of food in order to prepare a great feast—crops from the fields, and wild game from the forests—but they had no kettle to brew their ale. And what would a feast in Asgard be without ale?

But wise Odin cast the runes and discovered that Aegir, the giant who ruled the sea with his wife, Ran, had many brewing kettles. So Thor was sent to Aegir's hall on the island of Hlesöy. Thor was never tactful at his best, and since Aegir was a giant, the Thunder God didn't bother to ask politely for Aegir's help. Oh, my, no. Thor just tapped his giant-bashing hammer, Mjöllnir, in the palm of his hand and bluntly told Aegir that from then on the giant had to brew ale for all of the Aesir gods' feasts.

Needless to say, Aegir was deeply angered by Thor's rude demands, but he dared not refuse for fear of Thor's hammer. Carefully concealing his rage, Aegir put Thor off by telling him that he would gladly brew the ale . . . but, unfortunately, none of Aegir's kettles was big enough to provide drink for such a large gathering of Aesir.

Baffled, Thor returned to Asgard to report the disappointing news to Odin and the rest. No one knew where to turn next until Tyr the One-Handed spoke up: "Far to the east at World's End lives my father, the frost giant Hymir. He has a kettle there that reaches fully a league around the rim. Surely that should be large enough to satisfy even Aegir."

Thor agreed. "But do you think we can talk Hymir out of his kettle?"

"We can if we are cunning enough," replied Tyr. "Let's go."

So off to World's End went the two gods, riding in Thor's goat cart. When they reached their destination, they left the goats in the care of one of Hymir's field hands and entered the giant's hall. There they were greeted by Tyr's paternal grandmother, a grim-looking giantess with nine heads!

"Hi, grandmas."

"Why, look who's here, everybody; it's little Tyr. Hi, Tyr. Welcome home, Tyr. Where've you been, boy? Have they been feeding you enough? You look awfully thin."

"I'm fine, grandmas, really. Where's mother?"

"Here I am, son, and so glad to see you," said the golden-haired goddess who was Hymir's wife. "Your friend, Thor, is welcome, too."

She sat them down and served them frothing horns of beer. When they had emptied the horns, she said: "Hymir is due home at any minute, so I think you'd better hide under that big kettle on the floor over there until I have a chance to talk to him. He's often ungenerous with guests . . . and rather unpleasant about it, too."

Well, no sooner had Thor and Tyr concealed themselves beneath an overturned kettle than in stomped Hymir, icicles clinking in his frosty beard.

"Greetings, husband, welcome home. You'll never guess who's come to visit us—our son, Tyr, and his friend." Tyr's mother didn't mention Thor's name for good reason. "They're over there behind that pillar, just in case you were in a bad mood. But you aren't, are you?"

Hymir just grunted, then gave the pillar an icy stare. It immediately crumbled under his gaze and, one by one, eight kettles fell from the shelf it had been supporting. Each of them fell upon the kettle that sheltered the gods, and each one shattered—but not the one protecting Thor and Tyr, who then stepped forth to face Hymir. He turned his piercing gaze upon them, but recognizing who Thor was, Hymir abruptly decided to become a more gracious host. He ordered three oxen to be butchered and roasted for supper . . . and it was well he did, for Thor ate no less than two of them himself.

The next morning, Hymir told Thor that if they were to have any food for supper that night, it would be necessary for them to go fishing.

"There's nothing I'd like better," said Thor. "What do we use for bait?"

"I've got mine, Redbeard. You're welcome to find your own."

"Suits me." And Thor proceeded to kill Hymir's prize black bull with one blow of his hammer, then twisted off its head. "Let's see what this will catch."

Hymir turned pale, both with fear and rage, but he led the way to his fishing boat. Once there, he took the oars, while Thor sat in the stern. As for Tyr, since there really wasn't room for him in the boat anyway, he chose to remain in the hall catching up on the latest gossip with his lovely mother and many-headed grandmother.

Hymir rowed and rowed, until the little boat was many leagues out to sea, but each time he wanted to drop anchor and start fishing, Thor insisted that the giant row farther still. Finally the weary Hymir refused to row another stroke.

"Enough, Thor, enough. It's time we fished." And, in short order, the giant proudly hauled in two great whales. "Well, Thor, I've got my catch. Let's see if you can do as well."

The Thunder God said not a word but baited his huge hook with the bloody head of the black bull, then cast it into the depths of the sea—where it sank, and sank, and sank. It sank so deep, in fact, that it finally reached the watery realm of none other than the Midgard Serpent, that terrible old sea-dragon Jörmungand, who lay nibbling on the tip of his own tail, which just barely reached his head from way around on the other side of the world.

Now, when Jörmungand picked up the scent of the bloody bull's head, he let go of his own tail and—quick as lightning—his jaws clamped down on Thor's bait so hard that the hook stuck fast in the roof of his mouth. Well, what with Jörmungand thrashing around trying to dislodge that hook, and Thor hauling up the line hand-over-hand, it wasn't long before the Midgard Serpent's head came boiling up out of the sea looking around for the source of his trouble. Sure enough, there was this little boat bobbing in the waves, and there was Thor with his feet braced against the gunwale pulling as hard as he could on the line.

Hymir's face turned white with terror as the great sea-dragon's head poised above the boat. So, just as Thor picked up his hammer to throw it at Jörmungand, Hymir leaned over Thor's shoulder and cut the line with his knife. In the instant that Thor hurled his hammer, the line suddenly parted. Sna-p-p. Jörmungand abruptly fell back into the sea, and Thor tumbled onto his back in the bottom of the boat—so he never knew if his hammer had struck the Midgard Serpent or not before the beast disappeared beneath the waves. The hammer came sailing back to Thor's hand, as always, but Mjöllnir had no voice, so told no tales.

Thor was so furious at Hymir for cutting the line before Thor could make sure of his kill that the Thunder God struck the cowardly frost giant a mighty blow with his fist—Whack!—and toppled Hymir overboard. Then Thor hauled the sopping giant back in the boat and forced him to row them both back to the shore—with the two whales in tow behind them.

"It's all well and good for you to make me do all the rowing," grumbled Hymir sullenly, when they reached the shallows, "but you're going to have to give me a hand hauling ashore the boat and our catch. Which one do you want to do?"

Thor just gave the giant a disdainful look, then without saying a word, piled the whales on top of the boat and lifted the whole load onto his powerful shoulders. Without even breathing hard, Thor carried the boat and its cargo to Hymir's hall, where he deposited them at the giant's doorstep.

You would think that this remarkable show of strength would have made Hymir extremely cooperative, but when Thor and Tyr asked for his largest kettle, the giant said that he would part with it only if they could shatter his crystal wine goblet.

"Hmph. That sounds easy enough," said Thor, and taking the goblet in his hand, the Thunder God proceeded to hurl it clear through a stone pillar that held up the roof of the hall. But, when he went to retrieve the pieces of the goblet, he found it unbroken and without so much as a scratch on it.

"Not quite as strong as you thought you were, eh, Thor? Well, I'm feeling in a generous mood today. I'll let you have just one more chance. After you fail again, you can just go back to Asgard and leave me in peace."

Baffled, Thor looked around for something harder than the stone pillar at which he could throw the goblet. Just then Tyr's mother whispered: "Aim at Hymir's head, Thor. My husband is the most hard-headed man I've *ever* known!"

Thor could think of no better target, so he cocked his arm and hurled the goblet straight at Hymir's forehead. Crash! Tinkle! Shards of glass flew everywhere.

Beaten, but furious, Hymir growled: "Well, the kettle is yours, but you've still got to carry it out of here—if you can."

Tyr hastened to do just that, but none of his efforts succeeded in so much as budging the huge kettle. A sly smile played on Hymir's lips, as Tyr tried again—and failed again. Thor gently shouldered his friend aside and, with one mighty heave that caused his feet to crack the floorboards, the Thunder God hoisted the kettle onto his head and strode out of the hall.

Well, Hymir soon regretted his bargain, so Thor and Tyr had not gone very far when they heard a great clamor behind them. When they looked around they saw that they were being pursued by Hymir and a whole host of many-headed giants. Quickly Thor placed the kettle on the ground, and then he began to hurl Mjöllnir at the hapless giants. In no time at all, the hammer did its work and soon only Thor and Tyr remained standing.

Thus did Thor come face to face with the Midgard Serpent for the second time, as well as win the kettle of Hymir. Thus, also, did Aegir become—however reluctantly—brewer for the gods.

Thor's Duel with Hrungnir

Blundering into Asgard, the giant Hrungnir gets drunk and challenges Thor to a duel, a confrontation that will nearly end Thor's career.

One day, when Thor was off in the Ironwood hunting for trolls, Odin All-Father placed a golden helmet on his head, then saddled up Sleipnir—his great, gray, eight-legged horse. They galloped off to Jötunheim, the land of the giants, to see what adventures might befall them. After riding many uneventful leagues, Odin came to the hall of Hrungnir, mightiest of the tribe of hill giants. Hrungnir did not recognize the King of the Gods, but greeted him courteously enough—for a giant.

"Welcome, stranger. I saw you coming from a long way off. It seemed as if your horse barely touched the ground. He's a mighty fine steed."

"Indeed, he is. There's none finer in all the Nine Worlds."

"Heh, heh. You say that only because you've never seen my horse, Gold Mane, in action. He could run circles around your gray."

"I'll wager my head he couldn't. Shall we race?"

In reply, Hrungnir whistled up Gold Mane and vaulted into the saddle. And off they rode as fast as they could go. Up hill and down dale, and over mighty rivers the two horses streaked. Hrungnir had not exaggerated—at least, not much—Gold Mane *was* a magnificent race horse. But, as the leagues passed by beneath their pounding hooves, Sleipnir pulled steadily farther ahead.

So intent was Hrungnir on catching up with Sleipnir and his rider, that the giant failed to notice where the race was taking them . . . and the next thing he knew, they had passed through the gates of Asgard and reined to a halt before the very doors of Valhalla itself.

"A good race, Hrungnir, and well run. Now you must come into my hall and have some refreshments."

The Aesir gods were no less uneasy about hosting one of the feared giants inside their walls than Hrungnir was about being there all by himself. Still, when he observed that Thor the Giant-Killer was nowhere to be seen, Hrungnir relaxed a little and decided to make the most of this novel situation. Unfortunately, after he had downed two huge horns of ale, the drink went to his head and Hrungnir lost all caution and good sense.

"I like this hall of yours, Odin. Have half a mind to pick it up and carry it back to Jötunheim with me."

"Indeed, Hrungnir, and what would we do without Valhalla?"

"Oh, you wouldn't need it any more. I'd smash the lot of you flat, I would . . . except for Freyja and Sif. They're too bee-oot-iful for smashing. I'd find something better to do with them."

Well, with Hrungnir in this obnoxious mood, only Freyja was brave enough to continue pouring his ale.

"Thass right, pretty lady. You jus' keep on bringin' the ale. I'll drink every drop the Aesir have in the place."

At this point, who should come striding into the hall but Thor, just returned from his troll-hunting foray.

"What's this, what's this? A filthy dog of a giant drinking here in Asgard, and being served by Freyja, to boot? Who let him in, who granted him safe conduct?"

"Odin himself invited me here *an'* gave me safe conduct. So there."

"That's one invitation you may not even live to regret you accepted," growled Thor darkly, tapping his hammer in the palm of his hand.

"'S'all well an' good for you t' threaten an unarmed an' sozzled giant," Hrungnir hiccuped. "But small honor you'd gain if you killed me here and now. Are you brave enough to face me in single combat a week hence?"

"I can hardly wait," snarled Thor, and once they had agreed where to meet on the border between Asgard and Jötunheim, Hrungnir staggered back to Gold Mane and galloped homeward.

Much was made in Jötunheim of the impending duel when the other giants learned of it. Hrungnir was held in high honor for challenging Thor within Valhalla itself, but the giants also feared greatly what might happen should Hrungnir lose, for he was the largest and strongest of them. If Thor should kill Hrungnir, who among them could ever hope to stand against the Thunder God? So they made a giant of clay some nine leagues tall and three leagues across the chest, in the hope that such a sight would frighten Thor. The giants put a mare's heart in the clay creature's chest, magically brought him to life, and named him Mökkurkalfi. As for Hrungnir, his heart was of stone—as were his head and his shield—and his weapon was a gigantic whetstone, which he carried on his shoulder.

On the appointed day, Hrungnir and the clay giant went early to the dueling site to await Thor's coming. When they heard the distant rumbling of Thor's goat cart, Hrungnir lifted his stone shield up in front of him as a defense against Thor's hammer, Mjöllnir. Suddenly, Thor's servant, Thjalfi, rushed up and said:

"Oh, Hrungnir, Hrungnir, didn't you know,
Thor will attack you from down below?

If you'd win this fight, and life not yield,

Change your tactics and stand on your shield."

The gullible Hrungnir did as Thjalfi suggested, and thus he was unprotected when Thor came charging up in his goat cart amidst claps of thunder and flashes of lightning. Mökkurkalfi, the clay giant, was so terrified by this display of power that he promptly wet himself.

In the same instant that Hrungnir heaved his whetstone at Thor, the Thunder God cast Mjöllnir at the giant's stony head. Ka-blam! The two weapons crashed together in mid-air. The whetstone shattered, but one of the pieces struck Thor's forehead with such force that it knocked him to the ground. His hammer, Mjöllnir, was not deflected by the collision and hit Hrungnir squarely in the head, shattering his skull into as many pieces as his whetstone. Hrungnir's body toppled like a felled tree, and the giant landed with an earthshaking thump, one leg lying across Thor's neck, pinning the Thunder God to the ground.

Meanwhile, Thjalfi easily dispatched the hapless Mökkurkalfi, then tried to lift Hrungnir's leg off Thor's neck. Alas, it was too heavy for him to budge in the least. Just then, Thor's three-year-old son, Magni, came upon the scene and easily freed his father.

"It's too bad I didn't get here sooner, father. I'm sure I could have killed this nasty old giant with one blow of my little fist."

"Perhaps you could have, son, but this was my private fight. At any rate, I'm so proud of you that I want you to have Hrungnir's horse, Gold Mane."

Magni was well pleased with this generous gift, but Odin—who had just arrived on Sleipnir—was not. Odin felt that Thor might better have given Gold Mane to him.

Well, Thor went home to his hall, Thrudvang, but he still had a chunk of broken whetstone embedded in his skull. He sent for the wise woman Groa, wife of Aurvandil the Brave, who tried to remove the fragment by chanting magic verses. Sure enough, the stone started to come loose. Thor was so pleased that he made a big mistake. Instead of waiting to reward Groa until after she had finished her magic spell and removed the stone, Thor interrupted her chanting to tell her that he had recently rescued her husband from Jötunheim. The Thunder God had carried Aurvandil on his back in a basket across the icy river Elivagar back into Asgard. One of Aurvandil's toes had stuck out of the basket and been frozen solid, so Thor broke it off and hurled it into the sky where it became the star we know as Aurvandil's Toe. Thor told Groa that Aurvandil was on his way home and should be there by the time she returned. Well, Groa got so excited that she forgot the rest of the magic spell and rushed off to her home.

Thor never did get rid of that piece of whetstone and had to put up with it for the rest of his days. For that reason, one is forbidden to throw a whetstone across a room, for to do so would cause the piece in Thor's skull to move and give him a headache . . . and who would wish to do that?

Thor and the Giant Geirröd

What chance does Thor stand against a family of hostile giants without his magic hammer, iron gloves, and belt of strength? Help comes from an unexpected source.

Loki was, in a word, bored. So he borrowed the hawk-cloak of Odin's wife, Frigg, transformed himself into a great bird-of-prey, and rode the winds across the northern sky. His flight eventually carried him over Jötunheim where, seeing a strange castle he had never visited before, Loki descended in a broad spiral until he alighted on the ledge of a window set high in the castle wall. Peering down into the hall, Loki beheld the giant Geirröd looking back up at him.

The giant called out to one of his servants: "Climb up and fetch me that hawk. Never have I seen such a magnificent bird, and I must have it."

Well, Geirröd's servant was a good climber and soon reached the window. But just as he reached out to grasp the hawk's legs, Loki flapped up onto one of the rafters, and sat there as if to mock him. The servant looked at the hawk, looked down at the floor far below, thought about what Geirröd would do to him if he failed, and—with a gulp—climbed higher still. He straddled the rafter and started pulling himself hand-over-hand toward the hawk.

Loki just stared at the servant until he was almost within grabbing range, then tried to launch himself into the air and safety. Tried, I said, because Loki found that he could not let go of the rafter, try as he might. There he flopped and fluttered until the servant reached him, threw a bag over his head, and grasped him by the legs. At that point, the mysterious force that had trapped Loki's feet vanished, and the servant had no difficulty bringing the hawk back down to his master. Geirröd had the bag removed from the hawk's head, and stared intently into its eyes.

"Why, these are not the eyes of a hawk! This is some shape-changer come in hawk's form to spy on me. Tell me who you are— and quickly, if you know what's good for you. Tell me, I say."

But the hawk said nothing. Geirröd cajoled, Geirröd threatened; yet Loki remained silent.

"Stubborn bird! Think to defy me, do you? Let's see how you like being shut up in a chest for three months with no food and no light, and only your own droppings for company."

And it came to pass as Geirröd had decreed. Well, by the time three months had gone by, Loki was more than willing to tell his name and promise Geirröd anything, just to be set free. So it was that Loki scarcely hesitated when the giant told him that the price of his freedom was a promise to return to Geirröd's castle accompanied by Thor, but a Thor who was neither wearing his strength-multiplying Belt of Might nor carrying his giant-killing hammer, Mjöllnir.

The Eddas are silent as to what persuasion Loki used on Thor, but it must have been cunning, indeed, for it was not long before the two of them set off on foot for Jötunheim . . . and Thor went unarmed, as Loki had promised Geirröd he would. It was a long walk, and evening found the Thunder God and his companion still far from Geirröd's castle. They were, however, near the hall of the giantess Grid, who had borne a son—Vidar the Silent—to Odin All-Father. She gave them friendly greetings, a hot supper, and soft beds for the night. And, when Grid learned where they were bound, she privately gave Thor something else besides—good advice.

"I don't know what Geirröd may or may not have told Loki, but that giant is not to be trusted," Grid said. "Geirröd has ambitions to become foremost among the giant-kin, and what better way to do that than to kill the slayer of Hrungnir? But Geirröd is too clever to attack you directly, so beware, beware. Take with you my own Belt of Might, my iron gloves, and my staff. Grid's Rod is not so powerful as your own hammer, but it is the best I have to offer, and perhaps it will serve your needs."

Thor thanked Grid for her kindness, but he spent a restless night wondering what unpleasant surprises Geirröd might have planned for him. When Thor and Loki parted from Grid the next morning, and the Trickster saw what the Thunder God was wearing and carrying, Loki had a few uneasy moments.

"Still, that's not Thor's own belt," he reflected to himself, "and he doesn't have his hammer, so it's not as if I've broken my promise to Geirröd. And if something unpleasant were to happen to him, it would serve Geirröd right for treating me the way he did when I was a hawk."

That afternoon, Thor and Loki came to the broad, fast-flowing river Vimur, which lay between them and Geirröd's castle.

"Grab hold of my belt, Loki," said Thor, "and hang on for all you're worth. I'll use Grid's Rod to brace against the current, and we should be able to wade across without too much trouble."

Splish-splash, swish-swush. They had almost reached the far bank of the river, and were waist-deep in the main channel, when Loki let out a cry.

"Thor, Thor. The water is rising. It's a flash flood. We're going to drown!"

"Where could it be coming from? There's not a cloud in the sky."

Just then Thor looked upstream and spied Geirröd's daughter Gjalp straddling the river—to which she was adding at a prodigious rate.

"So that's the cause. Well, a river should be dammed at its source, they say." And even though the water was now nearly shoulder deep, Thor ripped a boulder out of the river bed and hurled it at the source of the flood. And he didn't fail to hit the target at which he threw.

When the Thunder God reached the far bank of the Vimur with Loki in tow, it was still touch-and-go whether or not he would be swept off his feet by the fierce current. But Thor was able to grasp the trunk of a rowan tree growing on the bank, and thus pull Loki and himself to safety. This is why we speak of the rowan as "Thor's salvation" and consider it to be good luck.

Now when Thor and Loki arrived at Geirröd's castle, the giant's servant showed them to the guest quarters—an old sheepfold—and told them they must wait there until his master was ready to see them. There was but a single chair in the place and, before departing, the servant told Thor that he was to occupy that place of honor.

Well, Thor had no sooner seated himself than the chair began to rise toward the ceiling at an alarming rate. Thor barely had time to thrust Grid's Rod against a rafter and push back as hard as he could. When he did so, there were two loud screams and the chair crashed to the floor—amid the moans and groans of Geirröd's daughters, Gjalp and Greip. They had been hiding beneath the chair with the intention of crushing Thor against the ceiling—but when he resisted so strongly, their backs were broken instead.

Then Geirröd summoned Thor into his hall and challenged him to a contest. Drawing a red-hot iron bar out of the hearth fire with a pair of tongs, the crafty giant hurled the glowing bar at Thor with all his might. The Thunder God plucked it out of the air with Grid's iron gloves, and prepared to return the throw. Geirröd ducked behind an iron pillar for protection, but Thor's cast was so powerful that the bar passed right through the pillar, through Geirröd's belly, through the castle's wall, and buried itself in the earth.

Thus perished Geirröd's plot to destroy Thor—and with it the giant himself.

The Apples of Idunn

The apples that Idunn gives the gods each day keep them from growing old. Disaster stalks Asgard when the giant Thjazi steals her away, and her apples with her!

It happened one day that Odin, Loki, and Hoenir had been wandering far from Asgard. It was getting to be late in the day, they had had nothing to eat since morning, and they were very hungry. The trio had seen nothing edible in the mountains, but as they came down into a beautiful valley they spied a herd of oxen grazing. Taking no heed of whose oxen these might be, the gods killed one and set about roasting it.

After a time, when common sense would tell you that the meat should have been cooked, they removed the roast from the fire only to discover that it was still raw. So they put the spit back over the fire and waited some more. After what seemed like a long time, the gods checked the roast again . . . and they were amazed to find that it was *still* uncooked.

"Hyaa, hyaa, hyaa," shrilled a voice from high in the tree beneath which the gods had built their fire. "Try as you might, you'll never get that fire to cook anything unless I give permission. This is my valley and my herd of oxen, and everything here—including fires—obeys me."

Then the travelers could see that the speaker was a giant eagle that had been resting atop the tree.

"We beg your pardon for killing one of your oxen without permission," said Odin, "but we saw no one to ask—and we really are very hungry."

"Oh, I understand, hyaa, and I won't even hold that against you. But, if you want the meat to cook, you must agree to let me eat my fill first . . . then, and only then, will the fire burn."

Well, the gods had no choice but to agree to the eagle's terms. Still, when it came spiraling down and seized the hams—the choicest part of the ox—Loki became so furious that he picked up his walking stick and whacked the eagle across its back. Then the most wondrous thing happened. The eagle screamed in pain and fury—hyaa, hyaa—and started to fly off . . . with one end of the walking stick attached to its back and the other end stuck to Loki's hands! He simply couldn't let go.

Loki was jerked off his feet and dragged along behind the eagle. Between the weight of Loki and the two hams, which the eagle still clutched in its talons, the bird couldn't fly very far above the ground, so Loki's shins and kneecaps banged against every boulder in the neighborhood. And, as if that weren't bad enough, the Trickster felt as if his arms were going to be pulled from their sockets.

"Oof, ow, oh, argh! Stop, stop, put me down, put me down!"

"Hyaa, I'll never put you down, little man, never. Unless . . . ."

"Unless what, unless what? Argh! Oh, ouch! I'll promise you anything, anything!"

"Will you, now? I wonder, but let's see. I'll put you down if you promise to bring Idunn and her Apples of Eternal Youth to the grove of trees that stands just beyond the gates of Asgard . . . and do it exactly nine days hence. Will you do that?"

"Yes, yes. Whatever you want. Only put me down now. Puh-*lease*."

"Very well. But just see that you keep your word."

And with that, Loki and his walking stick fell to the ground, and the giant eagle soared high into the air. "Hyaa, hyaa."

Loki limped back to meet Odin and Hoenir, who had been chasing after him and the eagle. He was pleased to see his companions, but when they asked how he had escaped, Loki made up a fanciful story because he dared not tell the truth.

Nine days later, Loki arranged to come upon Idunn at a time when no one else was about. He rushed up to her and blurted out: "Say, Idunn, you'll never guess what. It's quite the most marvelous thing. I was just wandering about in the wood, and I happened upon an apple tree I'd never seen before. It had the biggest, most beautiful apples on it. They looked so much like yours, I couldn't help but wonder if they, too, might not give eternal youth to whoever eats them. I knew you'd want to see them, so I hurried right back to fetch you. C'mon. Bring your apples along so we can compare them. Hurry up, it's not far."

Well, sweet, innocent, gullible Idunn was completely taken in by Loki's ploy. Carrying her basket of apples, she accompanied him through the gates of Asgard and into the grove where the Trickster had promised the eagle he would bring her. And, sure enough, there Thjazi was awaiting them—that's right, the eagle had a name, for he was none other than that mighty, magical, shape-changing giant in his bird form.

Before Idunn could utter more than a startled "eeek," Thjazi had seized her in his talons and flown off with her to his great hall, Thrymheim, far away in the mountainous wastes of Jötunheim. Perhaps Loki felt a twinge of remorse, but if so it was quickly overshadowed by a stronger sense of relief that he, at least, was now free of Thjazi's unwelcome attention.

Without their daily serving of Idunn's apples to rejuvenate them, the gods rapidly began to age. Gray hairs appeared where none had been before, and wrinkles began to furrow previously smooth skin. Backs became bent and footsteps faltering. Alarmed, Odin called a council to see if anyone might know what had happened to Idunn.

"When was the last time any of you saw Idunn?" croaked Odin.

"Why, I think I saw her going through Asgard's gate with Loki," one of the Aesir replied.

"Loki, eh? I might have known. Thor, you go and fetch him here." And Thor shuffled off to find the Trickster.

Well, it took only a few threats of unspeakable torture before Loki confessed what he had done. But he also hastened to assure the others that if Freyja would lend him her falcon cloak, Loki would fly to Jötunheim and try to rescue Idunn from Thjazi's stronghold.

It was a long flight, but luck was with Loki when he arrived at Thrymheim. Thjazi had gone off to the ocean on a fishing trip, leaving Idunn locked in a high tower. The giant knew she could not climb down, but you would think that a shape-changer who often traveled about as an eagle himself might have considered the possibility that his tower could be entered by another shape-changer in bird form.

Thjazi was careless, however, and Loki had no trouble flying right into Idunn's room. Before she even realized that it wasn't a real falcon sitting on the back of her chair, Loki had cast a spell transforming Idunn and the basket of apples to which she still clung into a nut. Grasping the precious nut in one of his talons, Loki launched himself out the window and began his flight back to Asgard.

Just then, however, Thjazi returned home. Seeing the falcon fly out from his tower window, the giant dropped his catch of fish, rushed up the stairs, and threw open the tower door. Idunn and the apples were, of course, nowhere to be seen. Thjazi rushed back down the stairs, grabbed his eagle-cloak from the chest where he stored it, threw it over his shoulders, and transformed himself into an eagle.

Then the chase was on! Loki had a good lead, but the eagle was a more powerful flyer, so league by league Thjazi slowly began to overtake the Trickster.

The gods, watching from atop the walls of Asgard, spied the two birds when they were still some distance away. Recognizing the falcon in the narrowing lead as Loki, the Aesir hastened—as fast as their infirmities permitted them—to gather up a huge pile of wood shavings just within the walls. As soon as the exhausted falcon had safely cleared the walls, the gods put a torch to the pile of shavings. Thus, the pursuing eagle was greeted by a tongue of flames that brought him plummeting—singed—to the ground. There the gods, enfeebled as they were, fell upon Thjazi and slew him in short order.

After Loki had regained his true shape, he transformed Idunn back to her natural form, too. She immediately gave her youth-restoring apples to all the gods, who were not at all sorry to rid themselves of the handicaps old age can bring. And from that day forth, the gods have never let Idunn out of their sight again.

Skadi's Choice

Thjazi's daughter, Skadi, arrives at the gates of Asgard demanding compensation for her father's death. But she'll only settle for a husband . . . and a good laugh.

The giant Thjazi, who had stolen the goddess Idunn and perished trying to get her back from the gods, had a daughter named Skadi. Not only was Skadi very beautiful, she was a great huntress—unmatched in her skills with the bow and on skis. Indeed, some even called her the Lady of the Skis.

A short time after Thjazi had been killed in Asgard, Skadi appeared before its gates—fully armed—and determined to avenge her father's death. Odin was struck by her savage beauty, and he felt some compassion for her loss, so rather than ordering Thor to crush her skull with his hammer, Odin offered Skadi whatever compensation she thought to be just.

"I will accept compensation, but you may not find it so easy to pay since I have no need for gold or silver. You have taken my father; now you can provide me with a husband. And," she added glumly, "I have had no reason to smile since my father was slain, so you must also make me laugh."

"Agreed, but with one condition," said Odin. "The gods will stand behind a curtain with only their feet showing—and you must make your choice on that basis alone."

Skadi thought that to be a very strange condition, but she agreed to abide by it. So the gods lined up behind a curtain, took off their boots, and poked their feet out under the curtain. Skadi walked back and forth, carefully looking at those feet with the skilled eyes of the huntress. Finally, Skadi pointed at the smoothest, whitest pair of feet she could find, sure in her heart that they must belong to Balder the Beautiful—the most handsome of the gods. Imagine her surprise when the curtain was pulled aside and out stepped her choice—Njörd, the grizzled old god of ships and fishing, whose feet were white and smooth from spending so much time in the water. Skadi was none too pleased, but she had agreed to the method of choosing so there was no help for it.

Then it was Loki's turn to try to make Skadi laugh. He tried everything he could think of—he made silly faces, he did animal imitations—but nothing worked. Finally, Loki took a long piece of thong and tied one end to a billy goat's beard and the other end to his own private parts. Then the Trickster began a tug-of-war with the poor goat. Both of them tugged and screeched, tugged and screeched—until the thong suddenly snapped, and both Loki and the billy goat fell down with a thump on their rumps. Well, the whole scene was so ridiculous that Skadi had to laugh in spite of herself. Thus Skadi was reconciled with the gods, and Odin set a sign and seal upon the reconciliation by taking her dead father's eyes and hurling them high into the sky to become stars.

But that's not quite the end of this story. When Skadi and Njörd were wed, they couldn't agree where they should live. She was a mountain girl, he a man of the sea. So, not surprisingly, Skadi wanted to live at her old home, Thrymheim, while Njörd preferred that they live at Noatun, his own hall on the seacoast. Both of them were strong-willed and neither of them would give in . . . so they compromised.

The couple agreed to spend the first nine nights at Thrymheim, the next nine at Noatun, and so on. That sounded like a workable solution, but when they went to her home, Njörd complained about the loneliness of the mountains and the haunting howls of the wolves that lived there. Then, when they moved down to Noatun, Skadi claimed that she could get no sleep at all because of the constant raucous cries of the seagulls. So Skadi and Njörd agreed to part company, and she went back to her beloved mountains alone.

Some say that, in time, Skadi married Thor's stepson, the god Ull, who shared her interest in the bow and skiing in the high mountains. But others claim that she became a wife of Odin, and that from them is descended the line of the famous Earl Haakon the Great.

The Death of Balder

Loki schemes to bring about the death of the beloved god Balder, and Balder's mother, Frigg, moves heaven and earth to try to bring her son back from the land of death.

Thor and Balder were Odin's elder sons, but—possibly because they had different mothers—the two gods looked nothing alike. Where Thor was stocky, Balder was tall and slender. Where Thor had flaming red hair and a ruddy complexion, Balder was so fair of face and hair that he seemed to radiate light. For this reason, he was sometimes called Balder the Beautiful. Thor had many nicknames, but Beautiful certainly was not one of them. The Thunder God was inclined to be gruff and quick-tempered, and more given to action than to deep thought. Balder, on the other hand, was without equal among the Aesir gods for wisdom, tact, and graciousness. Small wonder that he had no enemies . . . or so nearly everyone thought.

But there came a time when Balder began to suffer from bad dreams. These were real nightmares, night after night . . . and each of them ended with his death. Balder didn't know what to make of these ominous dreams, but because he was beginning to get dark lines beneath his eyes from loss of sleep and just plain worry, his wife, Nanna, urged him to tell his parents about them. When he did, Odin and Frigg both took the dreams seriously, but each of them reacted in a different way.

Odin, ever the deep thinker, wanted to know what the dreams meant. So he mounted his eight-legged horse, Sleipnir, and rode secretly to the barrow mound of a long-dead seeress who, during her lifetime, had had an unmatched reputation for being able to foretell the future. Mighty runes the All-Father cast beside her barrow mound, and in the end he called the seeress forth and forced her to prophesy for him before he allowed her to return to her grave. Thereafter it was a grim-faced Odin who rode back to Asgard, but he told no one of what he had learned—not even Frigg, who had ideas of her own about dealing with any possible threat to her son.

Frigg tackled the problem head on. She set about getting promises not to harm Balder from everything that could possibly do so: fire and water; iron and other metals; stones; earth; trees; birds; beasts; and poisons. If there were any beings who wished to slay Balder, they would be unable to find or make a weapon that would work against him.

When the other Aesir learned that Balder was protected against all weapons, they were greatly relieved—for everyone loved Balder. Soon one of the gods suggested that they honor their favorite kinsman by demonstrating his invulnerability for all to see. So they proceeded to throw stones at Balder, hack at him with swords, thrust at him with spears, and shoot at him with arrows. Sure enough, each time they did so, the weapon turned aside at the last instant and did not so much as bruise his flesh.

Oh, it was fine sport! There was much laughter and many cheers, and everyone was having a lot of fun. Well, almost everyone. Loki the Trickster—the Sly One—was not enjoying himself. He resented having someone else be the center of attention . . . and he decided to do something about it. Slipping away from the crowd sporting with Balder, Loki magically took on the form of a little, hunched-over, old woman and shuffled off to Frigg's hall, Fensalir.

"Pardon me, gracious lady. Could I trouble you for a drink of water?"

"Why, of course you can, grandmother. Is there anything else I can do for you?"

"Well, yes, there is. I had always heard that Asgard was a place of peace, but there's a bunch of gods attacking some poor young fellow out there. That doesn't seem right to me. Can't you stop them?"

"Ha, ha. It is kind of you to be concerned, grandmother, but you need not worry. That is my son, Balder, they are sporting with, and everything that could possibly hurt him has taken an oath not to do so. He is perfectly safe."

"Well, that's reassuring . . . if rather strange. Hmm, you say that everything has taken an oath, *everything*—without exception?"

"Well, there was one little plant, a mistletoe growing on that big oak tree you see just outside the gates of Asgard. It was too young to swear an oath."

"Oh, indeed, yes. And what harm could there be in anything that young, eh? Well, I thank you for your hospitality." And the old woman hobbled off.

But once there were no prying eyes to see him, Loki transformed back into his own shape and slipped through the gates of Asgard. The Trickster had no difficulty finding the oak tree and the little mistletoe that grew on one of its branches. Loki scrambled up into the oak, cut the mistletoe from the tree, then carved it into a little dart. Having done this, he hurried back to the place where the Aesir were having their fun with Balder.

Seeing Balder's blind brother, Höd, standing off to one side, Loki walked up to him and said: "Say, Höd, why aren't you taking part in the festivities? Why aren't you honoring Balder, too, by throwing a weapon at him?"

"Are you making fun of me, Loki? You know I'm blind. How could I possibly aim anything at my brother, assuming I even had something to throw—which I don't?"

"Well, this is your lucky day, Höd. I just happen to have a little dart here you could use. And I'll gladly tell you exactly where to throw it, if that will help."

"Gosh, Loki, that's awfully nice of you."

"Oh, think nothing of it."

So Höd, with Loki's help, hurled the little mistletoe dart right at his brother's chest . . . but instead of turning aside like the other weapons, the dart went straight to Balder's heart. His eyes and mouth flew open for an instant, then the most beloved of the gods toppled to the ground, dead. The crowd stood still in stunned silence, and Loki slipped away unnoticed, while Höd kept asking: "What's going on? What's happened? Somebody tell me, please."

When the Aesir realized what had happened, outrage replaced the silence, and they fell upon Höd and bound him so he could not escape—as if the poor fellow would have done so. The Aesir were bound by their own code of honor not to slay Höd in revenge, but the Eddas tell us that Odin's son Vali, who had just been born to the giantess Rind, soon carried out that vengeance for them.

Frigg was broken-hearted over Balder's death and, like many a mother after her, refused to accept the finality of it. Frigg went among the Aesir and vowed her eternal gratitude and love to whomever would ride to the land of the dead, and offer its ruler, Loki's daughter, Hel, a ransom for Balder's return. Many a stout heart quailed at the thought of entering Hel's frosty domain, but another of Odin's sons, Hermöd the Bold, agreed to go if his father would allow him to take Sleipnir. Odin agreed, and off Hermöd rode.

While Hermöd was traveling to Hel's abode, for even on Sleipnir it was a long journey, the other Aesir took Balder's body and placed it aboard his dragonship, Hringhorni, intending to put the ship to sea to serve as a floating platform for Balder's funeral pyre.

Unfortunately, the vessel was so large that they were unable to launch it from the shore on which it had been beached. Word was sent to Jötunheim, and very soon the giantess Hyrrokin arrived, riding on the back of a huge wolf and using a viper for a bridle. She leaped from the back of her wolfish steed, which was so wild it took the best efforts of four of Odin's berserkers just to hold it.

Hyrrokin put her shoulder to the prow of the ship and launched it with one mighty heave. So hard did she shove that the earth trembled and the rollers beneath the ship actually caught on fire from the friction of its passing. Thor grew angry at the violence of her actions, and he raised his hammer threateningly—but the other Aesir reminded him that Hyrrokin was only doing what she had been asked to do. Besides, they said, she had been promised safe conduct.

Now that the ship was afloat, the Aesir placed Balder's corpse on the pyre, surrounded by all those things he had treasured most in life. His grieving widow, Nanna, was so overcome by the sight that her heart burst on the spot, and she was laid on the pyre beside her beloved husband . . . inseparable in death as they had been in life.

Just before the pyre was set ablaze, Odin came aboard, whispered something in Balder's ear, then laid his own magic arm-ring, Draupnir, on his son's chest. When Odin went ashore, torches were thrust into the pyre, and—as the burning ship drifted slowly out to sea—Thor held aloft his hammer, Mjöllnir, to bless the funeral. A Dwarf named Lit, who was carrying on in a most disrespectful fashion, chose just that moment to run between Thor's legs. The outraged Thunder God, who had loved Balder very deeply, gave the Dwarf such a tremendous kick that Lit sailed out over the water and landed aboard the burning ship . . . and that was the end of him.

*   *   *

Meanwhile, Hermöd rode northward for nine nights, passing through many a dark valley as he proceeded ever deeper into the earth. Finally, Hermöd came upon the river Gjöll, which separates the lands of the living and the dead, and he rode out onto the glittering covered bridge that spans it. The guardian of the bridge, Modgud by name, asked Hermöd who he was and why—since he obviously wasn't dead—he was riding the Hel Way. Hermöd told Modgud that he was seeking Balder and asked if she had seen his spirit pass that way. Modgud assured him that Balder's spirit had already entered Hel's domain.

Thanking Modgud, Hermöd rode on until he reached Hel's Gate, where he was brought to an abrupt halt by the blood-curdling growls of Garm, the vicious Hound of Hel. Graww, graww! Fortunately, the dog was chained to the gate so it couldn't reach Hermöd and his steed; unfortunately, Garm barred their passage through Hel's Gate.

Hermöd was not called "the Bold" for nothing, however, so he backed Sleipnir off a few paces, then set the horse into a charge directly at the gate. Just as it seemed the horse and the hound would collide, Sleipnir leapt high into the air and sailed over the slavering jaws of Garm and over Hel's Gate as well.

Once beyond the gate, it was but a short ride to the hall of Hel, Queen of the Dead. There, indeed, Hermöd found Balder's and Nanna's spirits, and joyful was their reunion. But then an imperious voice cut through their merriment, and Hermöd turned toward the high seat to face the queen, Hel, herself.

"What are you doing here in my domain, Hermöd? You aren't dead . . . yet."

Hermöd paused a moment before replying, for the sight of Hel was enough to daunt the stoutest of hearts. One side of her face was fair to look upon—like her father's—but the other side was stomach-wrenching foul to see—like her troll mother's.

"I have come, oh, great queen, to beg you to let Balder return to the land of the living. Everyone and everything there grieves over his loss and prays for his return."

"Everyone and everything, eh? Somehow I doubt that. Still, I would not have it said that Hel is anything but just. This is what I will do, Hermöd. Go back to Asgard, and if you can, in truth, persuade everyone and everything to weep for Balder . . . why, then I will set him free. But there can be *no* exceptions. If so much as a single being or thing refuses to weep, Balder must remain with me forever."

Hermöd thanked Hel for her generosity, then spoke reassuringly to Balder and Nanna before riding off to Asgard. Balder asked Hermöd to return the arm-ring Draupnir to Odin as a remembrance, and Nanna sent along some gifts for her mother-in-law, Frigg.

As soon as Hermöd reached Asgard and reported what had happened, the Aesir sent messengers throughout the Nine Worlds to plead with everyone and everything to weep for Balder: "Oh, won't you weep for Balder, so that his bright face may light up our days once more? Won't you weep?"

And weep they did—oh, how they all wept. All living beings, the earth itself, and all things green and growing. Indeed, the grass weeps for Balder to this very day—its tears we call "dew." It seemed as if the wondrous deed had been accomplished, but as the last messenger was on his way back to Asgard, he came upon an old woman sitting at the mouth of a cave. And when he asked her to cry for Balder, she replied:

"Thokk weeps dry tears for Balder's death;
Dead or alive, I loved him not.
Let Hel keep what Hel hath."

Thus was Balder's doom pronounced, and the old woman—if that's what she really was—vanished right before the messenger's stunned eyes. When the Aesir heard of this, they were certain that the old woman had really been Loki in disguise. But the evil deed was done, and Balder was doomed to remain with Hel until the end of time.

The Binding of Loki

Loki tries to escape retribution for his evil deeds, but in the end he is caught and bound to a boulder deep in the earth, where Skadi has a special punishment in store for him.

The Aesir had tolerated Loki's mischief over the years because he was Odin's blood-brother, but the Trickster's role in Balder's death, his contriving to prevent Balder's return from Hel, and then his taunting the Aesir about these misdeeds . . . ah, these were the birch twigs that broke the reindeer's back. Loki realized that he had gone too far, so he fled Asgard and hid in the wilderness where he hoped the Aesir could not find him. On a mountaintop overlooking the sea, Loki built a hall with four doors so he could easily see if someone was approaching from any direction.

A rushing stream tumbled down the slopes of Loki's mountain and cascaded over Franang Falls before flowing out into the sea. Loki often turned himself into a salmon and hid beneath the falls, but he wondered what clever idea the Aesir might devise to capture him there. So, sitting before the fire in his hall, the Trickster tied pieces of twine together in such a way as to form a net, for it seemed to him that this might be what the Aesir would do—and by making one himself he might best be able to decide how to escape the device. Thus was created the first fishing net in the Nine Worlds.

But just as Loki finished making the net, he spied several of the Aesir coming up the mountainside toward his hall. The Trickster tossed the net into the fire and hurried down to the stream, where he once again took on the form of a salmon. When the Aesir rushed into the hall, they were dismayed to find that Loki had escaped them.

However, one of them noticed the pattern of ashes left by the burned-up net and deduced that it had been a device for catching fish. He told the others, so they then had not only a good idea as to where Loki was hiding . . . but how to catch him, as well. The gods proceeded to make their own net patterned after the one Loki had fashioned.

Then the Aesir descended the steep banks alongside Franang Falls and, once they were below the falls, stretched their net across the stream at their base. From that point they pulled the net downstream, hoping to catch Loki. But the clever salmon-man simply swam ahead of them for a little ways, then sank to the stream bed and the net passed over him.

The gods realized what was wrong, so they pulled up the net, put weights along its bottom edge, and tried again. Loki didn't want to be forced into the sea, so when he saw that he couldn't pass beneath the approaching net, he leapt over it and swam back to the base of the falls.

The determined Aesir marched back up to the falls and once more spread their net across its base, forcing Loki downstream toward the sea and all the dangers it held for a lone salmon. But this time Thor waded into the stream behind the net and followed along as it was moved. When the net neared the mouth of the stream again, Loki made a desperate leap across it . . . but Thor was waiting for him. The Thunder God grabbed Loki just in front of his tail fin and squeezed him so tightly that he couldn't wriggle free. And, do you know, salmon have kept that tapering shape to their tails ever since.

Well, the Aesir carried their captive—now back in his natural form—to a cave in deep, dark, misty Niflheim. There they transformed Loki's son Vali into a wolf, who then turned on his brother, Narfi, and tore him apart. The gods took poor Narfi's guts and used them to bind his father to a huge boulder within the cave. Once the bindings were securely in place, they were magically turned to iron.

The giantess Skadi had not forgotten Loki's part in bringing about the death of her father, Thjazi, so she fastened a viper above Loki's head to drip burning venom on his face. Loki's faithful wife, Sigyn, the mother of Vali and Narfi, was granted permission to sit by her husband's side with a basin to catch the venom. But she has to empty the basin whenever it fills up, and when that happens Loki writhes in pain as the venom hits his face. His agonized squirming deep in Niflheim is what causes earthquakes throughout the world. But in pain or not, bound is how Loki shall remain until Ragnarök, the Doom of the Gods.

Ragnarök, the Doom of the Gods

Unending winter, warfare, and despair grip the human realm. Bindings break; Loki and Fenris Wolf are free. The giants march on Asgard . . . it is the End of the Age!

When Odin All-Father raised the dead seeress from her barrow mound to learn of Balder's fate, she revealed not only that sad knowledge but far, far more. The seeress told Odin of the impending destruction of everything he had created and held dear—the Nine Worlds themselves.

The dead seeress spoke of the coming of Fimbul Winter—a time of blizzards and ice and frigid cold that will last for three long years, with no summers in between. During that period, human society will fall apart as families turn against each other and brother slays brother. The poets refer to it as "a Wind Age, a Wolf Age; an Axe Age, a Sword Age . . . the time before the Worlds end."

The close of Fimbul Winter will mark the beginning of the end, and will be signaled by the crowing of three roosters—Gullinkambi in Asgard, Fjalar in Jötunheim, and an unnamed bird in the halls of Hel. Then Heimdall will sound the Gjallarhorn and, as the hosts of Asgard assemble with their allies, the Light Elves, the world will shake and all bonds beneath heaven and earth shatter. Loki will go free, as will his son Fenris Wolf and Garm, the hound of Hel. Jörmungand, the Midgard Serpent, will crawl up out of the sea. Surt, Lord of the Fire Giants, will lead his kin out of Muspellheim. All will converge on the hundred-league-broad plain called Vigrid, which lies just outside Asgard . . . and the Final Battle will begin.

Odin will face Fenris Wolf, and the All-Father will be swallowed up by the beast he had deceived long years before. Odin's son Vidar the Silent will slay Fenris by ripping his jaws apart . . . but it will be too late to save his father, and so shall die the King of the Gods.

Frey will confront Surt, but having given up his magic sword as a bride price, the Sun God will have to defend himself with a deer's antler . . . and soon will fall beneath Surt's flaming sword.

Thor will face Jörmungand for the third, and final, time. Mjöllnir will finally crush the World Serpent's skull, but not before Jörmungand's venom finds its way to Thor's heart—and, after nine staggering steps backward, the Thunder God shall fall, dead.

Heimdall and Loki will fight each other to their mutual deaths, and one-handed Tyr and the Hel-hound Garm shall also be each other's doom. Surt will celebrate the victory of Chaos over the gods by swinging aloft his mighty sword and, in so doing, will set fire to all of the Nine Worlds. Even Yggdrasil, the World Tree, will succumb—and light up the whole sky before everything sinks beneath the sea, and all is silent. It will be the end of the Age.

But the long silence at last will pass, and one day the land will emerge again, fresh and green. The mountains will rise anew, and beneath the soaring eagle's wings, the glacier-fed streams tumble to the sea once again—it will be the dawn of a new Age.

The surviving younger gods—Odin's sons Vidar and Vali, and Thor's sons, Magni and Modi—will converge on Asgard to meet Hoenir, who will read the runes for the new Aesir. And Balder and Höd, returning from the dead, will join them. There on the grass by the overturned chess boards and fallen golden chessmen, which mark all that is left of Asgard, the new Aesir will ponder all that has passed before . . . and look to the future.

And, wonder of wonders, it shall come to pass that a man and a woman, Lif and Lifthrasir, having taken shelter within Yggdrasil's trunk, somehow survive the death and rebirth of the Nine Worlds. From them will come forth the new human race.

Has all of this taken place already, or is it yet to come? Only the dead seeress, sleeping beneath her barrow mound, knows for certain—and she isn't telling.

SECTION TWO:
THE NORTHERN PATH TO WISDOM AND BALANCE

FOREWORD: The Trailhead to the Northern Path

My inspiration for introducing the reader to the Northern Path—the wisdom quest envisioned by the ancient Nordic storytellers—grows out of my exploration of the Norse myths themselves and the extensive literature about them, as well as my personal experience as a "Viking" storyteller for a quarter of a century. On the one hand, my reading and study have revealed the intellectual complexity and spiritual insights that were invested in the stories. On the other hand, having presented the myths dramatically to live audiences of all ages and in a myriad of settings, I have experienced personally—and observed in my audiences—the inherent emotional power of the Norse myths.

Mythic storytelling is, at the very least, analogous to a spiritual ritual, but one that truly "works" only if both the "priest" (the storyteller) and the "congregation" (the audience) emotionally relive the story as it unfolds. Obviously this doesn't happen every time, but when it does—when the storyteller and the audience have tacitly agreed to "suspend their disbelief"—it can be a truly awe-filled experience. On occasion, I have, indeed, "wept for Balder," whose loss I felt at that moment as keenly as if he had been my own son.

Another example of the contemporary power of the Norse myths emerged during a scavenger hunt we held at the Sons of Norway heritage camp near Fall Creek, Wisconsin, the camp where I first had an opportunity to tell the myths and where I have done so most summers since 1980. In keeping with the camp's underlying emphasis on Norwegian heritage, the premise of the scavenger hunt was that the giants had stolen a number of the gods' treasures, including Thor's hammer. Thus Asgard was defenseless, and the giants were on the march! The campers' task was to search the campgrounds for the missing treasures and return them to Valhalla before the giants crossed the Rainbow Bridge into Asgard.

I will never forget the intensity with which some of the campers played the game. As time was running out and one or two of the treasures remained undiscovered, the feeling of urgency was palpable. Intellectually the campers knew this was a game, but emotionally they were convinced that the giants' invasion was imminent—and that only they could prevent it. For that brief hour, at least, the campers imagined themselves to be a vital, heroic part of something larger than themselves. Such is the power of myth.

My third and final example of the enduring relevance of the Norse myths comes from the same camp and, again, is associated with myth's ritual function. For some years we have had an honorary society at camp called the Fellowship of Yggdrasil, into which a camper is initiated when he/she has earned a prescribed number of *idrottir* ("accomplishments")[1] covering a wide variety of Viking-related athletic and/or intellectual activities.

On the final night of camp, after the rest of the campers are in bed, the inductees are blindfolded and led in total silence along a wooded trail to the far end of the athletic field and thence onto a long, high grassy berm called the "Barrow Mound" (the campers having been told it contains a Viking ship-burial). The inductees are stationed at intervals along the mound, and there they stand in the silence of the night, awaiting they know not what. After five or ten minutes, the silence is finally broken by the arrival of "Odin" and the three

"Norns," who first congratulate the inductees on their achievements, then ask them to pledge themselves to use their abilities for the benefit of the community and thus help to heal and sustain the World Tree. When they have so pledged, each inductee is asked to reach into a leather pouch that "Odin" is holding and to pull out whichever runic pebble "speaks" to him/her. At that point in the ritual, the inductee removes the blindfold, sees which rune has "chosen" him/her, and has its esoteric meaning interpreted by "Odin." After the last inductee has received his/her personal rune, the campers depart in silence for their cabins.

The effectiveness of the experience can be judged by the fact that even those inductees who are inclined to be more rambunctious in the course of daily activities take the ritual as seriously as their normally quieter peers. Anyone who has spent much time working with young teenagers knows how hard it can be for many of them to remain still and silent, but we have never had any trouble in this regard during the ritual. And, later, when their cabinmates ask them what went on, the inductees respect "Odin's" admonition to say nothing.

For my part, having served as "Odin" all these years, I can truly say that the combination of silence and solemnity beneath the starry "vault of heaven" has often filled me with awe—despite knowing objectively that I had created the ritual myself. But had I? It often seemed more as if I had subconsciously tapped into something much larger and more enduring. Again, such is the power of myth.

The combination of intellectual insights and emotional experiences I have derived from the Norse myths has convinced me of their contemporary significance and relevance. In order to share what I have found of value personally, I organized a workshop on the subject (which has been offered many times since its inception in

1988), and wrote a series of five magazine articles that appeared in *Viking* magazine[2]. A single, condensed version of those articles was published in *Scandinavian Press*[3] the following year and later reprinted as the Preface to my book *The Nine Worlds: A Dictionary of Norse Mythology*.

Also growing out of those articles was the major exhibition at the Vesterheim Norwegian-American Museum in Decorah, Iowa, called *Echoes of Odin: Norse Mythology in Scandinavia and America* (Sept. 2000-Jan. 2001), which my wife, Sharon, and I created and helped install. This book follows, in large part, the text of the exhibition, but greatly expands it in ways that would not have been appropriate for a museum exhibition, which must, of necessity, stress brevity.

You may be wondering: "Why yet another book about the Norse myths, and about their association with the runes?" It is true that there are some fine books available in bookstores and libraries, and I've tried to include most of the best ones written in English in the Bibliography. I think, however, that what *The Northern Path* has to offer is a unique perspective. It was not written from the viewpoint of an academic mythologist, nor that of an Odin-worshipper, nor of one seeking to use the runes to perform magic. Hopefully, persons who fit into any of those categories may still find something herein that can be of value to them. But the audience to whom this section of the book is aimed is one whose primary interest in Norse mythology is the opportunity it provides to explore the world view of the ancient Norse. Through the myths we can learn about their basic values, their hopes and fears, their sense of what the Universe is all about—and how we need to act accordingly. It is nothing less than the wisdom lore of the Ancient North that we seek along the Northern Path.

Finally, a word of caution to my readers. Be advised that this book is simply an introduction to the subject and is not intended to be exhaustive, nor to answer all your questions. Having seen the amount of disagreement that exists among the academic scholars on many points, it would be presumptuous of me to pretend that I know what everything means. I merely wish to point out the trailhead to the Northern Path; it is up to you to walk it for yourself.

CHAPTER ONE: The Nature and Relevance of Myth

To many scientists and other left-brained thinkers, we are now living—or ought to be living—in a post-mythological world. Such people have little use for anything that cannot be proven empirically. And, from a purely objective, scientific viewpoint, it is true we cannot prove that the passing on of our genes in the game of evolutionary roulette is not the only meaning to life.

However, for most right-brained thinkers—or for those who have succeeded in integrating both hemispheres of their brains—such a viewpoint is, to say the least, not very satisfying emotionally. We crave Meaning for our lives . . . and that craving leads us directly to Myth, a term that requires some clarification.

Contrary to common usage, myths are *not* falsehoods—intended to mislead—nor are they "make-believe" stories created solely for the amusement of children. While myths can be entertaining, they frequently focus on basic issues of human existence, and their meanings are often profound. Faced with the inevitability of our own death, as well as with recurrent threats to the society of which we are a part, we human beings turn to our cultural myths (the sacred stories of our people) for a sense of meaning and order.

A word of caution: mythic truths are metaphorical, not historical. They cannot be proven—or disproven—in an objective sense, like a chemistry experiment, but that does not justify dismissing myths as irrelevant. Their value lies in the human attempt to explore and explain those parts of the outer and inner worlds that do not yet—and may never—lend themselves to objective testing. Simply put, science attempts to answer the *what* and *how* questions of the universe, while the question lying at the heart of myth is *why*.

Joseph Campbell, who through his books and television interviews helped put us back in touch with our mythic roots, in his book *Myths to Live By* identified four basic functions of Myth:

> 1. The Mystical Function. To awaken and maintain in us a sense of awe and gratitude with relation to the transcendent, mystery dimension of the universe, whether that dimension is perceived as being "out there" somewhere or deep within the human psyche. The object here is not to create fear, but rather recognition and participation.
>
> 2. The Cosmographic Function. To provide a symbolic image (i. e., a mythic map) of the spiritual universe in accord with the knowledge of the times. Such a map is of inestimable value to us, whether we are pursuing shamanic practices or merely using active visualization as an aid to meditation.
>
> 3. The Societal Function. To validate, support, and imprint the norms of a specific moral order, i. e., that of the society in which we must live out our lives. In this way, we come to feel securely grounded within our community, and become productive members of it.
>
> 4. The Self-Integrative Function. To guide us through all of life's stages, from birth to death, in such a way that we are able to live in spiritual harmony with both ourselves and the universe. Myth-based rites of passage (e. g., vision quests) and role models (both positive and negative—some myths are

cautionary tales) are important aspects of this function.

"But," you may be thinking, "can Myth truly be relevant in a world of computers, microwave transmitters, and space shuttles? Is there really any place left for heroic gods and menacing giants?" While it is true that technology has changed dramatically over the past millenium, there is no evidence that the human psyche has done so as well. And the alternative to living our lives with a mythic perspective is to exist in a world seen in purely secular terms, with its mythic roots severed and no symbolic way to give meaning to the present. Thus humans become "naked in time," said mythographer John Greenway. In this psychological isolation, or alienation, our lives become purposeless and our deaths meaningless. A mythic universe, on the other hand, always has meaning.

In seeking to satisfy the mystical function cited by Campbell, many of us shallow-rooted European-Americans have been drawn to the myth-based world views expressed by Native Americans or peoples of the Far East. However, often there are significant problems encountered by non-Indians trying to embrace Native American spirituality or by non-Orientals attempting to become full-fledged adherents of an Eastern religion. Mythic systems arise within specific cultural contexts and, despite Campbell's contention that the face revealed behind each "Mask of God" is one and the same face, the masks *do* matter! Unless we can completely immerse ourselves in the culture that gave rise to the myths, it is difficult to successfully adopt a mythic system that is not a part of our own cultural heritage. This should hardly be surprising if we consider all four of the mythic functions elucidated by Campbell.

Each of us needs to feel as if we truly *belong* to some group, and the myths of our own people can help us connect spiritually and psychologically to our own lineage, to perceive of ourselves as being firmly "rooted" in an extended family—with ancestors and kinsmen extending back into the mists of time.

Many of us also want to feel connected to a special place. I will remember until my dying day the emotions I felt that summer evening I first visited the great fifth-century mounds at Gamla Uppsala in Sweden, the earliest known burial site for any of my ancestors. Being in the presence of their remains filled me with awe—I seemed to envision roots growing from the soles of my feet downward into the very bedrock of Sweden.

Fortunately for people of Nordic descent (those whose native tongue is in the Germanic language group), there is an ancient myth-based world-view that is theirs to claim by right of heritage—a philosophy as noble and earth-healing as those of the Far East or Native America. And it is not dead; it has only been forgotten for a time by many of its children. To begin recovering this world-view requires that we refamiliarize ourselves with Norse mythology. And what a rich treasure trove we have inherited! Tales of heroic quests, fearful monsters, magic swords, high ideals, low humor, love and lust, generosity and greed, the beginning and the end of all things—all are there for our pleasure and edification.

Not only can the Norse myths entertain us, but also connect us with our ancestors and reveal what they thought was really important in life . . . and just what it meant to be a human being. Once one delves into this mythology, one never looks at the world in quite the same way again.

Traditionally, the transmitters of Myth were the storytellers, and the most enduring story of all is that of the "Hero with a Thousand Faces," as Joseph Campbell has called that archetype. But the path of that hero is not meant to be trod only by the mythic archetype of each culture—it is the inner path that each of us must follow in living out the quest story of our own lives. We are constantly making choices (some good, some bad, some mixed, some indifferent) that alter our paths to some degree—great or small—and that can alter the paths of those around us. The details of the problems we face may have changed through time, but human nature has not—and moral choices are just as tough to make now as they ever were. If we are steeped in the myths of our own cultural heritage, if we recall the stories we have been told or read, our decision-making can become less confusing and our choices less lonely—for they will be rooted in the enduring wisdom of our ancestors.

Finally, we must consider whether or not Myth is a closed system, locked in the past, unchanged and unchanging. There is always the danger, as Campbell warned us, that we may concretize our myths—to take them literally rather than metaphorically. If we do so, we risk suffering from a "hardening of the intellectual and spiritual arteries" and stifling further growth, as well as opening ourselves to great turmoil (both internally and externally) when new information or insights impinge on our consciousness. Undoubtedly there will be new stories, with altered masks and new costumes, but I am confident that the archetypes and the core values they embody will remain essentially unchanged.

CHAPTER TWO: Sources of the Norse Myths

The Norse myths were the sacred stories of most of the Scandinavians (Danes, Norwegians, Swedes, Icelanders), as well as of the Germanic peoples of mainland Europe and Anglo-Saxon England. The Celts and the Saami, who live in parts of those same geographic areas, each had their own distinctive myths. The Finnish people—who shared territory and roots with the Saami, and were also neighbors of the Scandinavians—had yet another set of myths (published in book form as the *Kalevala* early in the nineteenth century). It is important to keep in mind that these cultures had social interactions over long periods of time, thus there is good reason to suspect that they influenced each other's mythologies to a greater or lesser extent (these influences—as well as those from Christianity—are discussed by Thomas DuBois in his *Nordic Religions in the Viking Age*).

Archaeological Sources: Although the Norse myths are popularly associated with the Viking Age (ca. 800-1100 A. D.) of Scandinavia, which certainly has been the richest source for archaeological material (to be mentioned later where pertinent), there is evidence that at least some aspects of Norse mythology originated much earlier.

For example, pictographic representations of the Norse World Tree have been found on a rock face in Bronze Age (ca. 1000 B. C.) Norway, and at the end of a runic inscription (ca. 400 A. D.) at Kylver on Gotland, Sweden. A miniature bronze Chariot of the Sun (ca. 1000 B. C.) was excavated in Denmark, and a runic inscription featuring the name of the god Tyr dates to the sixth century A. D. in Anglo-Saxon England. During the eighth century (just prior to the

Viking Age), various mythic scenes and symbols appeared on the huge picture stones that were erected on Gotland, Sweden. Finally, the oldest Thor's hammer amulet also comes from eighth-century Sweden. These examples are only a small sample, but they should suffice to demonstrate that the Norse myths were widespread in the Germanic North long before the Viking Age began.

Historical Sources: About 1075 A. D., Adam of Bremen, a German church historian, wrote a history of the archbishops of Hamburg in which he described—based on information provided by Swedish informants—the pagan temple at Gamla Uppsala, Sweden. Adam reported that the temple contained statues of the gods Thor, Odin, and Frey, to whom sacrifices were made. And every ninth year, the sacrifice included nine men—as well as nine males of each of seven kinds of animals—with all the bodies hung in a grove of sacred trees near the temple.

Literary Sources: The earliest surviving books featuring Norse myths were written early in the thirteenth century—a short enough time after the official Christianization of Iceland (where most of the myths were recorded) that there was still an active poetic tradition that lent continuity to the beliefs of the past.

One of the two Icelandic sources for Norse myths was the *Prose Edda* (or *Younger Edda*), which was written about 1220 A. D. by Snorri Sturluson (1179-1241), a prominent chieftain, poet, and historian. Snorri also authored *Egil's Saga* (the life of Egil Skallagrimsson) and *Heimskringla* (a history of the early kings of Sweden and Norway). All three books were monumental literary achievements.

The *Prose Edda* was written as a textbook to instruct budding skalds on the techniques and substance of skaldic poetry. Snorri related a whole array of Norse myths in prose form, then gave examples of how they could be used poetically—especially in brief phrases called *kennings*, which are literary allusions used to refer indirectly to what a poet really is talking about (e. g., "Freyja's tears" meant gold, or "the dragon road" meant the sea). Snorri was a Christian, but it is evident from his treatment of the mythic material that he retained an affectionate respect for the old stories and their characters. He clearly was familiar with many of the poems later collected in the *Poetic Edda*, as well as with seventeen or eighteen others—now, unfortunately, lost. The poems that contain the most wisdom lore are "Alvismal," "Grimnismal," "Havamal," "Svipdagsmal," and "Voluspa."

The *Poetic Edda* (or *Elder Edda*) is a collection of twenty-nine poems by various poets that was believed to have been assembled by an anonymous Icelandic compiler during the latter half of the thirteenth century. Although not written down until later than the *Prose Edda*, internal evidence suggests that some of the poems were originally composed at least as early as the Viking Age, hence the name *Elder Edda*. Half of the poems deal with myths of the gods, the other half with the legends of such Nordic folk heroes as Helgi Hundingsbane and Sigurd the Dragon Slayer.

There also is a Danish source from the early thirteenth century, the *Gesta Danorum* (a history of the Danes) by Saxo Grammaticus, which recounts a number of Norse myths and legends. Unlike Snorri, however, Saxo seems to have held a low opinion of the Norse deities, whom he diminished to human status. Saxo's stories differ from those in the *Eddas* not only in tone but often in detail, and they are not nearly so well known today as the Eddic versions (but see Poul

Anderson's *War of the Gods*, an imaginative retelling of Saxo's account of the life of the Danish folk hero Hadding).

A number of Eddic translations and modern retellings of the Norse myths are listed in the bibliography here. For many years, the most readable, comprehensive collection of retellings available in English has been Kevin Crossley-Holland's *The Norse Myths*, which also has an extensive section of notes for the reader who wishes to explore further. One needs to be aware, however, that in the interest of telling a good, coherent story, Crossley-Holland occasionally has embellished some of the details in the originals. The same cautionary note would apply to many of the other retellings, including the first section of *The Northern Path*, which contains the versions of the myths that I tell to live audiences.

One who seeks to delve into the mythic lore that would have been available to the ancient Norse must, of necessity, read and ponder one or more of the unabridged translations of the *Eddas*. When you do so, reflect on how the myths speak to you at whatever point you are in your life's journey. In interpreting what you read, be sure to remember that these stories were created by many different storytellers, over a period of many centuries before and after 1000 A.D., and in the context of societies that were different from our own. Hence the meanings that we are inferring may not be precisely what the first storytellers intended. But we need not be overly concerned about that possibility so long as the stories and symbols still have the power to move and inspire us.

CHAPTER THREE:
The Norse Mythic Worlds and Whence They Came

Although the Icelandic *Eddas* constitute a very small body of literature, they are rich in detail and imagery. Like other mythic systems, the Norse universe has a distinctive cosmography (a cosmic geography) and cosmogony (stories describing the origin of that universe).

> "Nine worlds do I know, the nine realms of the Tree,
> 'Neath the ground whence the great Ash rises."
> — *"Voluspa," Poetic Edda*

Our ancestors believed that there are Nine Worlds, arranged in three levels and all bound together by Yggdrasil, the World Tree (inside front cover). The upper and middle levels are also connected by Bifröst, the Rainbow Bridge. Each level contains a great spring (often called a well), and each of the worlds has its own unique set of inhabitants.

The Upper Level contains:
* Asgard—home of the Aesir Gods and Goddesses, as well as the warrior Dead.
* Vanaheim—home of the Vanir Gods and Goddesses.
* Alfheim—home of the Light Elves.

The Middle Level contains:
* Midgard—home of Humankind.
* Jötunheim—home of the Frost and Hill Giants.
* Muspellheim—home of the Fire Giants.

The Lower Level contains:
* * Svartalfheim—home of the Dark Elves (the Dwarves).
* * Niflheim—an essentially uninhabited world of ice, mist ... and dragons!
* * Hel—home of the non-warrior Dead.

Some scholars disagree with the placement of Muspellheim—thinking it belongs in the Lower Level—and they question if Hel is a distinct realm or merely a part of Niflheim, but not to recognize Hel as separate raises the question of what would be considered the ninth world.

A gigantic root of the World Tree extends into each of the three levels and the great spring that arises there: Hvergelmir in Niflheim, Mimir's Well in Jötunheim, and Urd's Well in Asgard. As we learned in the stories, Hvergelmir contains the water of creation, Mimir's Well the water of wisdom and understanding, and Urd's Well the water of healing for the World Tree.

The dragon Nidhögg dwells down in Hvergelmir, and Hraesvelg, a giant in eagle form, lives atop the Tree, where he causes the winds of the world whenever he spreads his great wings. A trouble-making squirrel, Ratatosk, runs up and down the trunk of Yggdrasil carrying insults between the dragon and the eagle—and who in the northern climes has not had the experience of being "scolded" by a red squirrel?

> "In ancient times, when Ymir lived,
> No sea nor land there was, nor lapping waves;
> Neither earth there was, nor heaven above;

Only a gaping void, and nowhere green."
—"Voluspa," *Poetic Edda*

How did these curious and complex worlds come into being? The Eddas tell us that two of them, Muspellheim and Niflheim, have always existed, and between them lay a yawning void called Ginnungagap. Poisonous rime ice formed on the rivers pouring forth from the great spring Hvergelmir in Niflheim, flowed out into Ginnungagap, and there came into contact with the sparks and embers hurled into space by the volcanoes of Muspellheim. Soon the ice began to melt, and the dripping fluid congealed to form the first being—Ymir, a sleeping giant. While he slept, the sweat gathering beneath his left armpit took the forms of a male and a female giant and, at the same time, his feet mated with each other—in some totally inexplicable manner—to produce a six-headed son[4]. Thus was the race of Frost Giants created.

During this time, Ymir was nourished by milk dripping from the teats of the cosmic cow, Audumla, who also had been formed from the melting ice. She, in turn, found nourishment by licking the salty blocks of ice. In so doing, however, Audumla freed from the ice the first man-shaped being who was not a giant. He was called Buri, and he later became the grandfather of the Aesir gods. Buri's son, Bor, married the giantess Bestla, and their three sons were Odin, Vili, and Ve—the first of Aesir.

The three brothers fell upon the sleeping Ymir and slew him[5]. So much blood flowed from his wounds that all of the Frost Giants drowned except for one family who managed to escape on something that floated, thus saving their race from extinction.

Odin and his brothers proceeded to drag Ymir's corpse into the very center of Ginnungagap, and there they dismembered it in order to create the rest of the Nine Worlds. From his flesh they made the earth, from his bones the mountains, from his teeth the rocks and pebbles, from his blood the sea and lakes, from his hair the trees, from his skull cap the vault of the sky (held up by four Dwarves—Austri, Vestri, Nordri, and Sudri—who were created from maggots feeding on Ymir's corpse), from his brains the clouds, and from his eyebrows a barrier between Midgard and the lands of the giants.

From sparks and embers blowing out of Muspellheim, the gods created the sun and the moon, the stars and the planets . . . and, at some point, they appointed charioteers (Sol and Mani) to guide the sun and the moon, respectively, on their daily paths. Sol and Mani are preceded daily across the sky by the chariots of Nott (Night) and her son, Dag (Day). Nott's horse, Hrimfaxi, bedews the earth each morning with foam from his bit, while Dag's horse, Skinfaxi, has so bright a mane that he casts light wherever he goes[6]. The chariots of the sun and the moon are chased across the sky by two giant wolves, Skoll and Hati Hrodvitnisson, who will catch the chariots and their precious cargoes at Ragnarök, the Doom of the Gods. These wolves are among the sons of the Hag of the Ironwood[7], a forest that lies east of Midgard and is rife with troll-women.

Odin, Vili, and Ve paused to survey their handiwork. As they strolled along the seashore one day, they came upon two trees (in the form of driftwood?) which they caused to take on the forms of a man and a woman, respectively. Odin gave these first humans breath and spirit, while his brothers gifted them with awareness and movement, and with speech, hearing, and sight[8]. The three brothers named the couple Ask (Ash) and Embla (Elm), and granted them all of Midgard for themselves and their descendants, the human race. Then, high above it all—whether atop the highest mountains or up in the sky—these first Aesir created their own homeland, the magnificent realm called Asgard, where they established their own steadings and erected their great halls.

It is interesting to note that in the Norse world view, the universe represents more of a transformation of previously existing matter than a creation from nothing—and that the gods themselves are early products of that transformation rather than its primary initiators. For that matter, if there was a prime initiator we are not told of it. There is no existing account of any directing consciousness behind that meeting of Ice and Fire in the midst of Ginnungagap which first produced life. The rime ice drifting out of Hvergelmir (the Well of Creation) contained the germ of life, rife with possibilities but lying dormant, awaiting the fire of Muspellheim to awaken that life and start it along the path toward its full potential. Ice and Fire eventually did meet, and thus began the mythic history of the Nine Worlds.

But all was not well in the Nine Worlds. The seeds of their destruction seem to have been present in their creation from Ymir's corpse. One threat to the existence of the Nine Worlds is posed by the constant hostility of the giants and trolls toward the gods and their allies—a hostility that may well have been rooted in the giants' resentment of the Aesir gods for assassinating Ymir. Margaret Clunies Ross, in *Prolonged Echoes: Old Norse Myths in Medieval Northern Society*, has suggested that another source of giant hostility may stem from their frustration at constantly being denied wives from among the goddesses, despite the gods having access to giantesses as wives/mistresses (e. g., Njörd-Skadi, Frey-Gerd, Thor-Jarnsaxa, and Odin with a myriad of giantesses). An interesting exception to this pattern is Loki, who, although he comes of giant stock, is allowed to wed the goddess Sigyn.

The giants are determined to overthrow and destroy the gods—a task in which they will be aided by the treacherous Loki and his monster sons, Fenrir (or Fenris) Wolf and Jörmungand, the Midgard (or World) Serpent. Much of what takes place in the myths reflects this menace and the sense of a slow, unavoidable movement toward the final, universe-shattering confrontation called Ragnarök, the Doom of the Gods, from which there will emerge no victor and few survivors.

CHAPTER FOUR:
"An Ash Tree I Know Called Yggdrasil ...."

What insights can we gain from the Norse myths into the ancient Nordic people's views of life? To answer that question, we must turn to Norse cosmology, to those stories and symbols that address the "why" of mythology.

> "An ash tree I know called Yggdrasil;
> The mighty tree's leaves are moist with dew
> That drips down into the dales below;
> Evergreen it stands by Urd's Well."
> —"Voluspa," *Poetic Edda*

Yggdrasil, the World Tree, which connects, supports, and protects the Nine Worlds, is one of the most powerful symbols in Norse mythology. In many ways, Yggdrasil seems to be a living metaphor of the harmonious, ordered universe. Yet the stories tell us that the Tree, on which all of life depends, is under attack from all sides. A twining of serpents or dragons—the ancient Norse made little distinction between them—lurks in Hvergelmir and gnaws[9] at the root that lies in Niflheim; four deer and a goat live in the branches of the Tree and browse on its leaves and buds, and the trunk is infected with a rotting disease. The biological realities of our own world clearly apply to the mythic worlds as well.

Close by Yggdrasil's great root in Asgard lies Urd's Well and the home of the three Norns (wise women, possibly of giant stock)[10]. Who are these Norns, and what is the symbolic significance of the Well and the Tree? Much of the following discussion is based on the thought-provoking ideas presented by Paul Bauschatz in *The Well and the Tree*, a book that deserves careful exploration by the interested reader.

The three Norns are named Urd (Fate), Verdandi (Becoming), and Skuld (Necessity). Urd knows all that has happened in the past, Verdandi sees everything that is taking place now, and Skuld foresees that which should necessarily follow from the events that the other two have observed. Together they weave the Tapestry of Fate.

Fortunately—and perhaps more importantly—the Norns also have taken on the task of healing the Tree. Each morning they mix the water from Urd's Well with the white clay from its bank to form a healing paste. This they spread on the trunk of Yggdrasil while they chant the *ørlög*, the essential and unchanging laws of the universe that both drive and limit the events taking place in our world. No record of the *ørlög*'s contents has survived, but after much reading and meditation (and drawing upon my observations of the natural world as a biologist), I would like to offer an educated guess as to what may lie at its heart:

"In the midst of darkness, light;
In the midst of death, life;
In the midst of chaos, order.

In the midst of order, chaos;
In the midst of life, death;
In the midst of light, darkness.

Thus has it ever been,
Thus is it now, and
Thus shall it ever be."

The Norns' action is not merely a symbolic acknowledgment of significant past events; it is meant to create and empower the present—in a manner comparable, perhaps, to the restoration and revitalization of the Dreamtime by Australian Aborigine elders when they chant the Songlines. So, too, did our Norse ancestors recite human laws at the beginning of each new session of the Althing, a Viking-Age judicial gathering. The past is not seen as something remote, inaccessible, and fading away—rather it is growing ever larger and more powerful as more events occur and more knowledge is accumulated.

If the Well is seen as a repository of the past, the Tree represents the present, depending upon the water of the Well both for growth and for healing. Thus the present is constantly influenced by all that has gone before. This active "power of the past upon the present" is sometimes referred to by the Anglo-Saxon term *wyrd*.

And, of course, the relationship between the Well and the Tree is reciprocal; once present events have taken place, their effects and implications drip like dew from the Tree back into the Well[11] to enlarge the past and further complicate and/or clarify it.

Clearly, the dynamic relationship between the World Tree and the forces of Chaos, kept in balance by the role of the Norns and the Well of Healing, reflects our ancestors' understanding that life is a struggle for each of us . . . and that we, too, need to respect the Tree and be part of its healing in our own world. This would appear to be the essential lesson that Yggdrasil teaches us. The relationship between

Order and Chaos in the Norse mythic vision of "the way things are" has been noted by many authors, most recently by Edward W. L. Smith in his 2003 article, "Of Thurs and Tyr," in *Parabola*.

Just to survive in this world, let alone live in such a way as to be favorably remembered after death, the wise person must learn as much as possible about the realms of the Well and the Tree. Thus one will come to glimpse—however dimly—the nature of *wyrd* itself, and to align oneself with it. In doing so, one will also contribute to maintaining the universal balance embodied in the *ørlög*.

This myth-driven quest for knowledge and understanding of the world and of oneself may well have contributed to the significant involvement of the Nordic peoples in exploration, natural history, physical science, philosophy, and psychology. Such a quest demands great personal sacrifice, however, and is always doomed to fall short of total enlightenment. After all, neither Odin's voluntary suffering on the World Tree—which won for him the secrets of the runes—nor his sacrifice of an eye to gain a drink from Mimir's Well of Wisdom succeeded in bringing to the King of the Gods full knowledge and understanding of the Nine Worlds, as we shall see shortly.

Recognizing and respecting the influence of the past upon the present, the Nordic peoples have always had a keen interest in family histories—not only their own but those of the other inhabitants of the Nine Worlds as well, and it is to the latter that we now turn.

CHAPTER FIVE: The Many Faces of Odin

Although foremost among the Aesir gods—and arguably the most knowledgeable being in the Nine Worlds—Odin is neither all-knowing, all-wise, nor all-powerful. And, at the end of the Age, he is doomed to meet his death at Ragnarök (see Chapter Ten). Still, Odin is undoubtedly the most complex being in Norse mythology, and the one whose activities form the axis around which the great mythic drama of the Ancient North revolves.

Despite being a gifted shapeshifter, Odin usually appears in the stories as a grey-bearded, one-eyed old man who is wearing a blue cloak and a broad-brimmed hat (perhaps to help conceal the fact that one eye is missing). To further obscure his identity during his wanderings, Odin almost always uses some pseudonym[12], especially when he is traveling alone. The meanings of most of the names characterize some aspect of his nature.

One of the names (or titles) that Odin bears is All-Father, reflecting the fact that he was a co-creator of Humankind as well as the actual father of most of the Aesir gods—among others. By his wife, Frigg, he had a son, Balder. Most of the other Aesir he sired are the offspring of various giantesses: Thor (by Jörd), Bragi (probably by Gunnlöd), Vali (by Rind), Vidar (by Grid), Heimdall (by nine sisters, the daughters of the sea giant Aegir and his wife, Ran[13]). Odin was also the father of Hermöd and Höd (whose mothers are never stated), as well as Tyr (according to the *Prose Edda*; the *Poetic Edda* says his father was the giant Hymir and his mother an unnamed goddess[14]). According to the "Ynglinga Saga" (*Heimskringla*), Odin fathered a number of sons—not listed among the Aesir—by the giantess Skadi after her marriage to Njörd dissolved.

No mention is made of Odin's having any daughters unless—as has been suggested frequently—Od is the name he is known by among the Vanir. In that case, he and Freyja had two daughters, Hnoss and Gersimi (or one daughter who went by two different names, having multiple names being a common practice in the Nine Worlds).

Another face of Odin is that of a god of war and of those warriors who die in combat. He is credited with starting the first war in the Nine Worlds (with the Vanir gods), and of instigating many human wars thereafter. When he began a battle, Odin would hurl his Dwarf-made spear, Gungnir, over the heads of the opposing army, an act said to cause fear and panic in their ranks. Odin was believed to be responsible for deciding who would live and who would die in any battle, thus when his favored warriors perished in combat, Odin was accused of betraying them—an accusation that to modern sensibilities seems just, and a behavior that strikes us as repugnant. Taken in context, however, All-Father's actions warrant a closer examination.

While conferring with the spirit of a dead seeress, Odin learned that a final confrontation with the giants is inevitable. In order to recruit an army large enough to have any hope at all of resisting the invasion of the giants, even temporarily, Odin brings the spirits of those who die in battle to dwell with him in Valhalla. There they fight each other all day, then are healed of their wounds so they can eat, drink, and carouse all night. Thus the *einherjar* ("lone fighters"), as they are called, maintain their fighting edge against the time they will be called upon to defend Asgard.

We can see, then, that—rather than being wicked and capricious—Odin's "acts of betrayal" are engendered by his pragmatic response to a real need to fill the ranks of the *einherjar* with the best warriors available. This undoubtedly was of little comfort to Odin's worshippers, who anticipated that their allegiance to him guaranteed them victory every time they engaged in combat, but at least it should absolve All-Father of the charge of treachery. His followers simply chose to follow a very demanding god!

We cannot leave our discussion of Odin as god of battle and the fallen warriors without mentioning the Valkyries, the Wild Hunt, the berserkers, and human sacrifices. The Valkyries are warrior women whom Odin has assigned to ride through the sky to scenes of battle and to carry the dead fighters back to Valhalla. There the Valkyries assume the role of serving maids to welcome the dead heroes to their new home.

Throughout the Germanic world, there was a long-standing belief that Odin leads an army of the dead on horseback through the stormy winter sky. In later times, the Wild Hunt came to be associated with the Twelve Nights of Yuletide. In leading the Hunt, presumably Odin rides his famous eight-legged horse, Sleipnir, a son of Loki.

The berserkers ("bear shirts") were bands of especially ferocious warriors, dedicated to Odin, who worked themselves into such a state of battle frenzy (possibly with the aid of some mind-altering drug—but not the fly-agaric mushroom, which has a different effect) that they often chewed on the rims of their shields. When they "went berserk," they felt little or no pain and were almost impossible to bring down with anything less than a killing blow. Naturally, the berserkers were greatly feared by warriors who had to face them.

Human sacrifices (usually of slaves or prisoners-of-war) were made in Odin's name, the victim first being hung, then stabbed with a spear, thus ritually re-enacting All-Father's self-sacrifice on the World Tree. None of the existing tales specifically refers to Odin's demanding these sacrifices but, as many of the victims would enter the ranks of the *einherjar*, he probably was not unhappy to get them.

Another face of Odin—and the one that probably will resonate most with many readers of this book—is that of a seeker after wisdom. Soon after he and his brothers, Vili and Ve, created most of the Nine Worlds, Odin undertook three dangerous and painful quests in order to gain knowledge, wisdom, and the gift of being able to communicate effectively what he learned to others. I believe these three Odinic quests exemplify essential lessons the Northern Path has to offer each of us who wishes to follow his or her own *wyrd*.

Quest One: Odin on the Tree—The first quest led Odin to be hung on Yggdrasil for nine nights in order to learn the secrets of the runes, ancient Nordic letters that symbolize hidden knowledge (see Chapter Nine). All-Father described his Nordic "vision quest" experience in the poem "Havamal" (*Poetic Edda*), as quoted in the story "The Trials of Odin". Because of this experience, Odin is sometimes called the "Hanged God" or "God of the Gallows."

Quest Two: Odin at Mimir's Well—Realizing that knowledge without understanding is not only less than satisfying but may even be dangerous, Odin traveled to Jötunheim to visit the Well of Wisdom, which was guarded by his maternal uncle, the giant Mimir[16]. There, at the cost of one of his eyes (for achieving wisdom always comes with a high price), All-Father was granted a drink from the Well. Since Mimir is said to drink the water of the Well thereafter from Odin's Pledge, i. e., his eye (*Prose Edda*), it is not inconceivable that Odin may have done so himself. In any event, in drinking the waters of wisdom, All-Father gained the inner vision (insight) and understanding that allowed him to make the best use of the knowledge he had gained from the runes.

Quest Three: Odin and the Mead of Poetry—Having drunk from Mimir's Well, All-Father must have come to understand that his acquisition of knowledge and wisdom, while obviously enriching him personally, did little for the society of which he was a part, over which he ruled, and for the well-being of which he bore primary responsibility. To achieve their maximum benefits, knowledge and wisdom must be shared—not hoarded like dragon's gold! To accomplish this, one must develop the skill to communicate effectively with others, which was the focus of Odin's third great quest—his search for the Mead of Poetry, one of the longest myths that has come down to us.

To briefly summarize the story, following the war between the Aesir and the Vanir, the two sides performed a rite of reconciliation[17] in which each of the gods spat into a vat (the saliva was believed to contain the essential nature of each individual), and from the spittle they created Kvasir, the wisest of all beings (because he contained the wisdom of all the gods). Two wicked Dwarves, Fjalar and Galar, murdered Kvasir and drained his blood, which they mixed with honey to create the Mead of Poetry (also known as Kvasir's Blood). Overreaching themselves by subsequently killing the parents of the giant Suttung as well, Fjalar and Galar had to give him the Mead as his parents' blood-price (monetary compensation for a murder being a common practice in Viking times).

Suttung hid the Mead in a cavern deep within the mountain called Hnitbjörg, and installed his daughter, Gunnlöd, as its guardian.

Disguised as a handsome young giant, Odin seduced Gunnlöd and persuaded her to let him have a sip of the Mead. When she did, he swallowed it all, changed himself into the form of an eagle, and—barely eluding pursuit by Suttung, also in eagle shape—flew back to Asgard. There Odin shared the Mead with the other gods and with some humans. To this day, whoever tastes the Mead gains the gift of poetry and eloquent speech.

If we look closely at Odin's three quests, we find—as a number of authors have noted previously—that All-Father was performing the role of a shaman in each of them. And we are told that Odin learned (from Freyja) and practiced seid (or seith), a form of magic most scholars now equate with shamanism. Clunies Ross has pointed out that this decision on Odin's part also required a sacrifice, inasmuch as seid was considered to be unmanly, presumably because the shaman assumes a passive (i. e., feminine) role in allowing himself to be possessed by a spirit or spirits. Men who are in touch with their *anima* (the feminine aspects of their personality)—and who have suffered bullying because of their sensitivity—can surely identify with Odin's position.

Since the general public usually does not associate shamanism with ancient Nordic spirituality, I think it will be worthwhile to review the key features of shamanism briefly, at least insofar as it relates to Norse mythology.

Shamanism is probably the world's oldest form of spiritual expression involving a specialized practitioner. Although specifics may vary among cultures, a shaman (a North Asian term) is one who enters a trance[18] in order to send his soul to the invisible spirit world to gain insights or, perhaps, to recover the soul of a sick person. The shaman anticipating a spirit journey to a point somewhere on the face of the earth usually will start from some isolated, elevated place (such as a pole or tree—like Yggdrasil—or, perhaps, Hlidskjalf, Odin's high throne that allowed him to see what was going on anywhere in the Nine Worlds). On the other hand, a journey to the underworld often begins beside a tree root (like Mimir's Well) or a hole in the ground (such as the one Odin, in snake form, crawled through to reach the heart of Hnitbjörg).

The shaman's spirit may travel alone or in the company of spirit helpers. In some cases, a spirit helper may face psychic dangers on the shaman's behalf[19]. These spirit helpers were sometimes thought of as being extensions of a person's soul, and in the ancient Nordic world were called *fylgjur* (singular *fylgja*, literally "a follower"). Non-shamans had them, too, but usually could see their *fylgjur* only in dreams, if they were gifted with "second sight," or were nearing the moment of their death. The *fylgja* also has been referred to as a "fetch;" a person who sees his fetch is said to be "fey" and is believed to be doomed. Some mythologists have argued that Odin's ravens, Hugin ("Thought") and Munin ("Memory"), who bring him news each day from throughout the Nine Worlds, are actually his *fylgjur*[20]. Odin is said to fear that his ravens might not return, a fear that can be appreciated by any elderly person faced with the possible loss of his or her own thought and memory.

As ruler of the gods, Odin presides over meetings of the Aesir. Thor, Balder, Tyr, Bragi, Heimdall, Höd, Vidar, Vali, Ull, Forseti, Hoenir, and Loki are the twelve usually mentioned as being present. But "Skaldskaparmal" (*Prose Edda*) substitutes the Vanir Njörd and Frey for Balder and Höd—and one wonders what became of Odin's brothers, Vili and Ve, who surely should have been numbered among the Aesir. All of these gods, as well as the more prominent Asynjur (associated goddesses), are the subject of the next chapter.

CHAPTER SIX: Odin's Family—The Aesir and Asynjur

Thor: Second only to Odin among the Aesir, in terms of power and responsibility, Thor was one of the three most popular gods during the Viking Age—the other two being Odin and Frey. Thor remains popular today, even starring in his own long-running Marvel comic book series.

Thor Redbeard is the god of thunder, who rides through the storm clouds in his goat cart (whose wheels produce the rumbling sound of thunder) and causes rain to fall on the lands below. It is only fitting that his wife is Sif, the golden-haired goddess of grain, with whom he has a daughter, Thrud. His role in helping to bring about bountiful crops does much to explain his special popularity among Viking Age farmers, who also probably approved of his reputation as a big eater and drinker.

Thor's other role is to defend Asgard (and, by extension, Midgard and us humans) against the incursions of giants and trolls, who greatly fear his magic hammer, Mjöllnir. Whenever Thor hurls the hammer, it strikes whatever he aims at with the force—and effect—of lightning. He wears a belt of strength that increases the velocity and impact of each throw, and Mjöllnir flies back to him with such force that Thor must wear iron gloves just to be able to catch it. Because of his success against giants and trolls, miniature Thor's hammers were popular amulets during the Viking Age, and replicas are occasionally seen today adorning necks in northern Europe and America. Mjöllnir has sometimes been used to sanctify weddings (the most famous example appearing in the myth "The Theft of Thor's Hammer").

Also symbolically associated with Thor is the rowan (mountain ash) tree. While crossing a river on his journey to the hall of the giant Geirröd, Thor was nearly swept away by a flash flood (caused by one of Geirröd's daughters, who was using the river as an outhouse). Thor managed to save himself—and his companion, Loki, who was holding on to Thor's belt—by grasping a rowan that grew beside the stream. Ever since, the rowan has been called "Thor's salvation." According to Clunies Ross (in an article appearing in U. Dronke et al., *Speculum Norroenum: Norse Studies in Memory of Gabriel Turville-Petre*), the Saami equivalent of Thor, Horagalles, has a wife named Ravdna ("rowan tree"). Rowan berries were said to be sacred to her, and from medieval times onward they were used as protection against witchcraft and dark magic.

Thor's special nemesis is Loki's son Jörmungand, the Midgard Serpent, whom the Thunder God first encountered during a series of contests of strength Thor faced—and failed to win—when he visited the castle of Utgard-Loki, a giant king wise in magic. The second time Thor and Jörmungand faced each other was during a "fishing expedition" that the Thunder God took with the giant Hymir. Thor was prevented from killing the Midgard Serpent only because the terrified Hymir cut the line that held the sea dragon to the boat. Thor and Jörmungand are fated to meet one last time at Ragnarök.

In the scenario just described, it seems clear that Thor acts as a representative of Order, and the Midgard Serpent a representative of Chaos. Their first two encounters are standoffs, a reflection of the dynamic balance that exists between Order and Chaos, and which I believe lies at the heart of the *ørlög*. So long as this balance is maintained, the Nine Worlds will continue to exist. Should Thor finally prevail over the Serpent of Chaos, nothing could ever change, stagnation would set in, and all possibilities for future creativity would cease. Should Thor be slain, Order would totally disintegrate, and the Nine Worlds with it. Alas, the Eddas tell us of yet a third possibility, a final confrontation between the two adversaries at Ragnarök (the Doom of the Gods) in which both will be slain . . . and the Nine Worlds consumed by fire and flood (see Chapter Ten).

Thor's ongoing personal warfare with giantkind, which he often carries into Jötunheim itself, has resulted in the deaths of a multitude of giants and giantesses. Yet his mother, Jörd, is a giantess, as is Jarnsaxa, the mother of his sons, Magni and Modi. Thor's attitude toward giantesses is ambivalent, to say the least.

Frigg: Odin's principal—and perhaps only official—wife is Frigg, goddess of marriage and motherhood, the one whom women invoke for her aid in childbirth. Despite her role as the champion of socially approved love, there is one story that tells of an occasion when Odin was absent from Asgard for an extended period of time, and his brothers, Vili and Ve, shared both his throne and Frigg's bed. And Loki hasn't let her forget it!

Balder, Höd, Nanna and Hermöd: It isn't clear how many children Frigg and Odin have in common, but Balder certainly was their first-born son and the heir to Asgard. At a crucial point in the cosmic drama, Frigg attempted to ease Balder's fears about his impending death (brought on by a series of horrible nightmares) by taking oaths not to harm Balder from all the weapons and potential weapons in the Nine Worlds. To celebrate Balder's seeming invulnerability, the Aesir took turns casting missiles at him—none of which touched him because of the oath. All was well until Loki tricked Frigg into revealing that a certain sprig of mistletoe hadn't taken the pledge (because it was too young to swear an oath). Loki made a dart from the mistletoe, then persuaded the blind god, Höd, to throw it at his brother Balder, and it killed him on the spot. Thus, for the first time, death came to one of the Aesir.

While the gods were preparing for Balder's cremation at sea[21], his wife, Nanna, died of a broken heart and was laid upon the funeral pyre with him. Before setting fire to the pyre, Odin placed his magic arm ring, Draupnir, on his son's chest and whispered something in his ear. The substance of that message remains one of the most intriguing mysteries in the Norse myths, although several writers have suggested that it had to do with Balder's eventual resurrection.

Meanwhile, Hermöd—yet another brother—rode Sleipnir down into Hel's domain to plead with the Death Goddess for the return of Balder's spirit to Asgard (yet another shamanic journey?). Hel agreed to do so if every single thing in the Nine Worlds would weep for Balder. Frigg sent out messengers to all quarters to see that this was done, and so beloved was Balder that it seemed for a time this quest would succeed. Unfortunately, there was one person—an old woman, Thökk (almost surely Loki in disguise)—who refused to weep, so Balder has to remain in the Land of the Dead until the end of the Age.

Forseti: Forseti, the god of justice, is the son of Balder and Nanna. He is also one of only a handful of third-generation gods mentioned in the myths.

Bragi and Idunn: Bragi is the god of poetry, and Odin's son, probably by the giantess Gunnlöd. Bragi's wife, Idunn, is the custodian of the Apples of Youth. On one occasion, she and the apples were kidnapped by a giant with nearly disastrous results for the gods (see Chapter Eight).

Heimdall: Heimdall is the guardian of Bifröst, the Rainbow Bridge. He can see as well at night as during the day, and his hearing is so keen that he can hear grass growing. When the invading giants start to march over the Rainbow Bridge to attack Asgard, Heimdall will blow the Gjallarhorn to warn the Aesir.

When Midgard was still quite young, Heimdall (using the name Rig) wandered widely in that land and fathered the three classes of society that were known during the Viking Age—thralls (slaves or serfs), karls (free farmers), and jarls (nobles)—thus giving a mythic justification to the social order.

Heimdall has teeth of gold (which make for a dazzling smile), and the ram is his special animal. He is a good friend of Freyja, and helps to defend her against Loki's mischief. On one occasion, Heimdall fought Loki—both of them in seal form (or were those their shamanic spirit helpers?)—to regain Freyja's necklace, the Brisingamen, which the Trickster had stolen from her.

Tyr: Tyr is a god of war, but he is best remembered for having sacrificed his sword hand in order that Fenris Wolf might be bound (see Chapter Eight). Tyr is a role model *par excellence* of courage and sacrifice on behalf of his community.

Ull: Thor's stepson, Ull, is unique among the Aesir in being a god of winter. He is credited with creating the first skis (his favorite form of transportation), and he is also the god of archery. "Ull's boat" is a kenning (a condensed metaphor) for a shield, so one has to wonder if there might not have been a long-lost tale in which Ull used his shield to travel on water. Warriors engaged in a *holmgang* (single combat, usually on a tiny islet from which there is no escape) pray for Ull's protection. Turville-Petre (*Myths and Religion of the North*) says that the most solemn of oaths during the Viking Age were those sworn on Ull's ring.

Vali: Vali the Avenger, the son of Odin and the giantess Rind, executed Höd for his part in the death of Balder[22], supposedly when Vali was only a day old!

Vidar: Vidar the Silent is destined to avenge Odin's death at Ragnarök (see Chapter Ten). He is said to be the strongest of the gods after Thor.

The Asynjur: Aside from Frigg and Idunn (as well as Freyja, after she came from the Vanir as a hostage), the Asynjur—the female counterparts of the Aesir—play very minor roles in the great mythic drama of the North. Indeed, some writers have suggested that many—if not most—of them are merely personifications of Frigg's various attributes.

Saga seems to have no role beyond drinking each day with Odin from golden cups in her large hall, Sökkvabekk. Eir is said to be the best physician. Gefjon (or Gefjun) is said to be a virgin, and all women who die virgins become her handmaidens. Gefjon has the gift of prophecy. Fulla is also a virgin, which is why she wears her hair uncovered. She looks after Frigg's wardrobe and is her confidante.

Sjöfn turns the thoughts of men and women to love, and it is from her name that the Old Norse word for love (*sjafni*) comes. Lofn is a kindly soul and obtains permission from Odin and Frigg for men and women to marry, especially those who have been forbidden to do so previously. Var listens to vows pledged between men and women, and she punishes any who break their vows.

Vör is so wise and inquisitive that no secret can be kept hidden from her. Syn is the doorkeeper who keeps out those who have no right to enter the hall (presumably Fensalir, Frigg's abode). She is also appointed defense counsel in law cases where the defendant wishes to deny the accusation. Hlin is assigned to look after those men whom Frigg wishes to protect. Snotra is so wise and gentle that any person exhibiting those attributes of moderation is said (in Old Norse) to be *snotr*. Gna is Frigg's messenger, who travels everywhere on her horse, Hofvarpnir, which can run over the sea and through the sky.

Also sometimes counted among the Asynjur are four giantesses, Thor's mother, Jörd, Vali's mother, Rind, Frey's wife, Gerd, and Njörd's wife, Skadi, as well as the goddesses Sol and Bil, whose daily journeys tend to keep them far from Asgard. Sol guides the Chariot of the Sun (discussed previously) and Bil rides in the Chariot of the Moon. Bil and her brother, Hjuki, had been carried off by Mani when they attempted to climb a hill to fetch a pail of water as he was passing overhead in his chariot. This episode gave rise to the old nursery rhyme about Jack and Jill.

The names of still other goddesses sometimes appear in a list of the Asynjur, but apparently they were not considered to be a part of the core group. It seems that membership in the Asynjur may have fluctuated situationally, rather than being a constant.

CHAPTER SEVEN: The Vanir Gods and The Elves

The Vanir—Gods of Fertility

The Vanir are generally regarded as being the Norse fertility gods—whether it be the fertility of plants, of animals, or of human beings. No surviving myth tells us how or where the Vanir originated, although some mythologists have speculated that they were the resident deities of a more-or-less peaceful, matriarchal society of farmers and fisherfolk whose lands were invaded by an aggressive, patriarchal group of Aesir-worshipping pastoralists. Those mythologists go on to suggest that the Aesir-Vanir war recounted in the myths probably was a reflection of the clash between the two human cultures in early Scandinavia. It is an attractive explanation, but almost surely is overly simplified.

Be that as it may, the conflict between the Vanir and Aesir arose because of the treatment of a Van woman who was visiting Asgard. The stories tell us that Odin, fearing Gullveig was about to corrupt the Aesir with gold lust, had her speared and then burned. But Gullveig survived this treatment—not once, but thrice—and went on to become Heid and practice witchcraft wherever she went. The Vanir were outraged by the Aesir's breach of hospitality, and the war between them commenced, ceasing only after the walls of Asgard had fallen.

At the end of the war, as part of the reconciliation process, the Van Njörd and his two children, Frey and Freyja[23], went to live in Asgard as a surety against further hostilities. The Aesir sent Hoenir and Odin's uncle, the wise giant Mimir, to Vanaheim in exchange. This exchange did not work out very well for the Vanir. Although Hoenir was a good-looking fellow, he seemed to be incapable of answering any questions directed to him without first being advised by Mimir. The Vanir concluded that Hoenir was a useless dolt and that they had been cheated . . . so they cut off Mimir's head and sent it back to Odin! All-Father magically preserved his uncle's head and continues to confer with Mimir as the need arises. The logic of the Vanir's action seems inexplicable to us today.

Njord: Njörd is a sea god and governs the sea winds and fishing. Hence he is prayed to by fishermen for favorable breezes and bountiful catches.

In the best known story about Njörd, he was chosen as a husband by the giantess Skadi in partial compensation for the slaying of her father, Thjazi, by the gods. The gods stood behind a curtain, so Skadi had to choose her mate by the appearance of his feet alone. Njörd had the whitest feet (from spending so much time in the water), which made Skadi think they belonged to Balder. Thus she wasn't very happy when the curtain was pulled aside to reveal her choice.

For the first nine nights of their marriage, Njörd and Skadi stayed at Thrymheim, her home in the high mountains. Njörd complained that he couldn't live there because the howl of the wolves kept him awake all night. So the next nine nights they stayed at Noatun, his home by the sea. There Skadi couldn't sleep because of the raucous cries of the gulls, so the two of them went their separate ways.

Frey: Frey is a sun god who governs the fertility of the crops and livestock on which human prosperity depends. He also promotes peace, in which the other activities can flourish and be enjoyed. The boar is Frey's special animal.

On one fateful occasion, Frey sat upon Odin's forbidden high seat (Hlidskjalf) so he could look out over all the Nine Worlds. Frey saw the beautiful giantess Gerd way off in Jötunheim . . . and he fell madly in love with her. So lovesick was Frey that he could neither eat nor sleep, so he sent his servant Skirnir to court Gerd for him. Win her Frey did, but he had to give up his magic sword as a bride-price—and that will serve him ill at Ragnarök (Chapter Ten).

Freyja is the goddess of passionate love, and it is to her you should pray in order to gain the love of the object of your affections. The myths tell us that Freyja is desired by many a god, giant, and Dwarf. Still, her only known husband is called Od—whom many scholars think is actually Odin, and by whom she has two daughters, Hnoss and Gersimi. When her husband leaves her to go a-wandering, Freyja weeps tears of pure gold (or possibly amber). She owns a famous necklace—the Brisingamen—which was made for her by four Dwarves, allegedly at the price of spending one night of love with each of them. The necklace was later stolen by Loki, and recovered by Heimdall.

Freyja works a powerful kind of magic called seid (or seith), which she has taught to Odin. Freyja often travels in a chariot drawn by two large cats, hence the later association of cats with female magic workers. Like many Norse deities, Freyja has the ability to shape-change; she owns a feathered cloak that allows her to transform into a falcon, and in one story she took on the form of a sow. Half of the dead warriors who go to Asgard will dwell with Freyja in Folkvang rather than with Odin in Valhalla.

The Elves—Light and Dark

Closely associated with the gods—and usually thought to be allied with the forces of Order—are the two races of Nordic Elves, the Light and the Dark.

The Light Elves (*Ljösalfar*) are the most mysterious beings in the Nine Worlds. We know the names of almost no individuals—although they are often mentioned as a group—and no stories have survived in which they play an active role. Light Elves are fair of face[24], and they are devoted to the world of sunlight (their term for the sun is "fair wheel"), blue skies, and growing plants. The Light Elves are fond of music and dancing, and they are reputed to be fine weavers. The bow is their weapon of choice, although apparently they use it primarily for hunting; none of the existing stories characterizes them as being aggressive or violent. They are thought to be very wise and spiritual in nature.

During the Viking Age, ox-blood or milk was offered as a sacrifice (*alfablot*) to the Light Elves in matters involving fertility and child birth, and also for healing. The offerings were poured into cup-shaped depressions in stones, which lay in close proximity to a sun-wheel symbol. Some writers have supposed that the Light Elves represent the spirits of dead humans, but the *Ljösalfar* are not associated with the Underworld as are the Celtic Elves. The highly spiritual nature of the Light Elves might account for their being the only ones allowed to dwell in Gimle—the gold-roofed hall in the highest level of the heavens—prior to Ragnarök, when the righteous Dead may join them.

Having no wings and not being tiny in stature, the Light Elves should not be confused with the fairy folk of some other cultures. If, as some ancient sources imply[25], the Norse concept of the Light Elves was inspired by the Saami people of northern Scandinavia, then they would have stood nearly five feet in height. The Elves portrayed by J. R. R. Tolkien in his novels *The Hobbit* and *The Lord of the Rings* probably come close to appearing as the ancient Norse imagined the Light Elves to be.

The Dark Elves (*Svartalfar*) are more commonly known as the Dwarves (*Dvergar*). Snorri says that their faces are "darker than pitch" (hence the name Dark Elves), but that would be inconsistent with what we know of creatures living underground, which usually are pale-skinned. I cannot help but wonder whether the light-dark distinction between the two groups of Elves might not have referred originally to where they lived rather than to their complexions. The Dwarves are quite short, rarely attaining a height of three feet. They live underground in Svartalfheim, whence they do not venture out except at night—exposure to sunlight causes permanent blindness[26]. One story, "Alvissmal" (*Poetic Edda*), does tell of a Dwarf being turned to stone by sunlight, but usually that was a fate reserved for trolls.

The Dwarves are the master metalworkers of the Nine Worlds, crafting everything from magic swords to exquisite jewelry . . . often for the gods. Some of their most famous work includes:

* Brisingamen—Freyja's necklace;
* Draupnir—Odin's arm-ring that produces eight rings just like it every ninth night;
* Gleipnir—the magic fetter used to bind Fenris Wolf;
* Gullinbursti—Frey's golden-bristled boar that can run through the sky by day or night;

* Gungnir—Odin's spear that causes fear and panic in any army over which he throws it.
* Mjöllnir—Thor's hammer that never fails to strike that at which it is thrown;
* Skidbladnir—Frey's foldable ship that always produces its own favorable wind.

The Viking-Age Norse attitude toward the Dwarves was decidedly ambivalent. Although the little people can be quite helpful—especially when they stand to gain by doing so—they can also be spiteful and malicious (e. g., Fjalar and Galar, who killed the wise Kvasir as well as two elderly giants).

The great writer of Northern epic fantasy J. R. R. Tolkien drew all of his Dwarves' names from the list included in "Voluspa" (*Poetic Edda*). Another name from that same list, Gandalf ("magic Elf"), Tolkien gave to his Odinic wizard.

CHAPTER EIGHT: Foes of the Gods

Giants and Trolls

From the time of Creation—when the Aesir gods killed Ymir, the first giant—the giants and gods have existed in a state of mutual hostility. It is a conflict the gods started, and one which Thor perpetuates; the stories often tell of his being off in the east killing giants and trolls. This conflict will lead eventually to the destruction of the Nine Worlds at Ragnarök.

The giants vary greatly in size, but one saga indicates that the males are about fifteen feet tall, the females about twelve feet. Giants also vary in appearance, intelligence, and disposition. Some of them—especially the males—could be ugly, slow-witted, and ill-tempered, but many of the giantesses are very attractive (Frey's wife, Gerd, for example). Some giants are very wise (Mimir) or adept at magic (Utgard-Loki), and it is in Jötunheim that the Well of Wisdom lies. Giants may be referred to in Old Norse as *jötnar*[27], *thursar*, or *risir*, but these names apparently do not correspond to the three distinct groups of giants mentioned in the Eddas—the Frost, Hill, and Fire Giants. In fact, it has been suggested by Jakob Grimm (*Teutonic Mythology*) that all giants descended from Ymir should be called Frost Giants due to the unique manner in which he was created.

Some of the more notable giants are:

Aegir—lives on an island in the sea with his mermaid wife, Ran. They gather the treasures that are lost at sea when ships sink. He brews the best ale in the Nine Worlds.

Geirröd—forced Loki to bring Thor to Geirröd's castle without Mjöllnir, his iron gloves, or his belt of strength. Aided by the friendly giantess Grid, Thor was able to prevail against the giant and his murderous daughters, Gjalp and Greip.

Hrungnir—after losing a horse race to Odin, he got drunk in Asgard and foolishly challenged Thor to a duel. Hrungnir's skull was shattered by Mjöllnir, but a piece of the giant's huge whetstone was lodged in Thor's head forever after. According to Grimm (*Teutonic Mythology*), all subsequent whetstones are derived from fragments of Hrungnir's original weapon.

Hymir—rowed Thor out to sea to "fish" for the Midgard Serpent, but he cut the line before Thor could strike the great sea dragon with Mjöllnir. Later Hymir lost his ale cauldron to the god when Thor smashed the giant's "unbreakable" crystal goblet on Hymir's hard head.

Thjazi—in eagle form, dragged Loki across rocky ground until the Trickster agreed to help him abduct Idunn and her Apples of Youth. When the rapidly aging gods forced Loki to steal her back, Thjazi followed and was burnt to death inside the walls of Asgard.

Thrym—stole Thor's hammer and said he'd return it only if Freyja would marry him. Thor dressed up in her bridal gown and veil, and he turned the giant king's wedding reception into a slaughterhouse.

Utgard-Loki—was not related to Loki the Trickster although he, too, was a clever shape-changer. Undoubtedly the greatest wizard among the giants of Jötunheim, Utgard-Loki could magically move mountains and castles, make the Midgard Serpent look like a cat, and give humanoid form to wildfire, his thoughts, and old age.

Trolls, while essentially giantlike in size (a few are scarcely larger than humans), are always ugly, stupid, and thoroughly unpleasant to be around . . . and what's more, they eat human flesh! Some trolls also differ from giants in having a tail and as many as nine heads (very few giants have extra heads). A many-headed troll woman named Gryla is mentioned in the Icelandic *Sturlunga* saga as having fifteen tails! Most later legends make no comment as to whether or not trolls possess one or more tails, but in "Cat on Dovrefjell," the Norwegian folklore collectors Asbjørnsen and Moe explicitly state that some trolls have long tails while others—like giants—have none at all. Moreover, some troll-women have such a long nose that they can use it to stir the stew pot.

Unlike giants, trolls can only go out at night because sunlight turns them to stone. Indeed, folklore tells us that many of the mountains of Norway are really trolls who forgot to get into their caves before sunrise. Typical of these ancient trolls were Stallo, the eternal nemesis of Lapland's Saami people, and Grendel and his mother, Danish monsters of such awesome strength and ferocity that only a hero of the stature of Beowulf could have hoped to overcome them.

In the modern Norwegian language, the word "troll" has come to be applied to all supernatural beings (not just trolls, but the huldrefolk, nisser, and other nature spirits as well[28]) and, for that matter, to anything magical or bad (with the implied assumption that magic *is* necessarily bad). For example, the Norwegian word for wizard is *trollmann*, and *trollunge* is a term sometimes applied to a naughty child. Similarly, in Swedish, a Saami shaman's drum is called a *trolltrumma*.

An interesting cultural (and psychological?) phenomenon of the twentieth century has been the progressive "sanitization" of the Troll in Scandinavia, where the species has persisted long after the last giant disappeared. Homely still—but usually smiling, and often reduced to a less-threatening size—trolls are found nowadays on T-shirts, postcards, posters, sidewalks, and souvenir store shelves throughout Scandinavia. Most recently, trolls have even been subject to widescale commercialization in America by Danish toy manufacturers, whose non-traditional products are garishly adorned with idiotic grins and rainbow-colored hair. What a sad fate for the grim monsters of forest, fen, and fjell—to be softened from a cautionary figure of terror into a gentle, or even cute, nature spirit who is often portrayed as being downright friendly or, at worst, mischievous.

Perhaps such treatment reflects humankind's conviction that it has "conquered and tamed" the natural world. If so, we may be in for a rude awakening: recent hurricanes, floods, earthquakes, ice storms, and avalanches have clearly shown that the forces of Nature can still bring us to our knees, quaking in fear. No, we have not tamed the Troll, only indulged in wishful thinking . . . while trying to ignore the ancient sense of being watched by *something* when we walk alone in the deep woods. If we can recapture a healthy respect for untamed Nature, perhaps the true figure of the Troll will re-emerge, and a new generation can thrill to the feel of the hairs rising on the back of their necks when they sit around a campfire and hear the storyteller conclude: "So long as there are trolls, you are never truly alone in the dark"—a wonderful quotation from Elizabeth Boyer's novel *The Sword and the Satchel*.

Loki the Trickster

Except for Odin, Loki is clearly the most complex character in Norse mythology. A giant by birth[29], Loki became Odin's blood brother (none of the stories tell us why) and spends most of his time in Asgard. It has been suggested by several writers (e. g., Alice Karlsdottir in her 1991 article "Loki, Father of Strife," *Gnosis Magazine)* that Loki represents the shadow side of Odin, but it strikes me that Odin has enough of a shadow side to his own personality that he doesn't need Loki to take on that role for him.

Loki is a clever trickster (a cultural figure who keeps a society from becoming set in its ways by acting contrary to the rules). Many stories tell of his first getting the gods into predicaments—and then getting them out again.

After the war with the Vanir ended, Asgard's wall needed to be rebuilt. Loki talked Odin into making an unwise bargain with a wandering stone mason, who later was revealed to be a giant in disguise. Odin promised payment of Freyja, the sun, and the moon if the job was completed, because Loki said the deadline would be impossible to meet. The stone mason's horse, however, was a fantastic aid to his master, and the job was almost done when Loki (in the form of a mare) distracted the stallion long enough that the wall was not finished on time. That is how Loki came to have an eight-legged horse, Sleipnir, for a son.

Loki and Thor were often traveling companions, but one memorable story has them at odds. As Thor's wife, Sif, lay sleeping, Loki lopped off the long golden hair that was her pride and joy. Thor was red-faced with anger and demanded that Loki make things right. To do so, Loki traveled to Svartalfheim where he persuaded two

Dwarves—the unnamed Sons of Ivaldi—to make new tresses of living gold for Sif. While they were at it, they also made some marvelous presents for Odin and Frey. In a rare blunder, Loki bet his head with another Dwarf, Brokk, that he and his brother, Eitri, could not make finer gifts for the gods. Among the precious wonders they crafted was the hammer Mjöllnir for Thor, which caused Loki to lose his wager. Through a clever legal maneuver, the Trickster managed to save his head, but Brokk won the right to sew Loki's lips shut.

In the earlier stories, Loki's pranks were merely annoying, but later his behavior took a turn for the worse. Eventually, he brought about Balder's death. To punish Loki, the gods bound him to a rock in Niflheim, and Skadi fastened a viper above the Trickster to drip venom on him. When it hits his bare flesh, he shudders and we have earthquakes. Loki's faithful wife Sigyn tries to catch the venom in a basin—and does get most of it—but she has to empty the basin from time to time.

Loki's Children

Loki fathered three strange children by Angrboda, a giantess (troll-woman?) who lived in Jötunheim. When the gods learned about them, they carried the children off to Asgard so they could keep an eye on them while they were growing up.

The oldest of these children is Jörmungand, the Midgard Serpent. Jörmungand soon grew so large that the gods feared what he might do. So Odin cast him out of Asgard, and Jörmungand fell down into the world ocean. There he continued to grow larger and longer until one day he finally encircled the world . . . and met his own tail!

When Thor visited the giant Utgard-Loki, the Thunder God met the grown-up Midgard Serpent for the first time, although Jörmungand was disguised as a cat! Thor tried to lift him free of the floor, and of course he failed.

Thor was very unhappy with the outcome of his first meeting with the Midgard Serpent, so he coerced the giant Hymir into helping Thor go "fishing" for Jörmungand. Using a bull's head for bait, Thor did succeed in hooking the great sea dragon, but a fearful Hymir cut the line before the monster could be hauled close enough for Thor to use his hammer.

Thor and Jörmungand are fated to meet for a third, and final, time at Ragnarök.

The second child of Loki and Angrboda is a daughter named Hel. One side of her face is fair like her father's, but the other side looks like that of a mouldering corpse. This circumstance probably gave rise to the expression that someone "looks like Hel," a comparison with a place—the Christian realm of torment—not making nearly as much sense.

Because of Hel's gruesome appearance, the gods couldn't stand to look at her. So Odin sent her down to Niflheim and gave her rule over all those who die a "straw death" (i. e., in bed rather than in battle). They are not being punished there, but are not rewarded either.

There is, however, a region in Hel's domain called Nastrand, which is reserved for the spirits of oathbreakers, seducers of other men's wives, and murderers. The hall in which they dwell has walls woven from the bodies of living serpents, whose venom flows like rivers through the hall—rivers that the inhabitants of Nastrand must wade. It seems more than coincidental that Loki, who brought about the death of Balder, also is doomed to face an eternity of viper venom burning his flesh.

Loki's third offspring with Angrboda is Fenris Wolf. Like his brother Jörmungand, Fenris soon grew so large that the gods feared he might decide to eat them. They couldn't kill him, for that would have violated their own law of hospitality (and, presumably, they remembered what happened the last time they had done that—when their attempt to slay Gullveig triggered the Aesir-Vanir War). So the gods tricked Fenris into letting them bind him so he could "show how strong he was."

Much to the dismay of the gods, Fenris broke the first two fetters they placed on him. Lest they fail altogether, Odin sent Frey's servant Skirnir to Svartalfheim to ask the Dwarves to make a magical binding. This they did, using some very special ingredients (the sound a cat makes when it walks, hair from a woman's beard, the roots of a mountain, the sinews of a bear, the breath of a fish, the spittle of a bird).

Fenris was suspicious of the magical binding and refused to let the gods put it on him until one of them agreed to place his hand in the wolf's mouth as a surety against trickery. In a sacrificial act of great courage, Tyr volunteered. Thus it came about that Fenris was bound—and will remain so until Ragnarök—and Tyr lost his right hand.

CHAPTER NINE: Runestones and Dragons

Runes: Mystic Alphabet of the Ancient North

No surviving monuments from ancient Scandinavia cast a more romantic aura than the runestones, large rocks inscribed with letters from a mysterious alphabet and the figures of strange beasts (especially dragons) or scenes from Norse mythology (e. g.: Odin riding his eight-legged horse, Sleipnir; Odin about to be swallowed by Fenris Wolf; or Thor fishing for the Midgard Serpent). The romantic element undoubtedly reflects the association of the runic alphabet with magic, a notion clearly put forth in the *Poetic Edda* (in the poems "Havamal," "Rigsthula," and "Sigrdrifumal") and perpetuated by such modern tales of high fantasy as J. R. R. Tolkien's *The Lord of the Rings* (which is firmly rooted in Germanic mythology)—not to mention a rash of New Age "how to" books.

Runic inscriptions on wood, bone, stone, and metal date from as early as the first century A. D. About 5,000 inscriptions have been found, most of them in Sweden—although the oldest surviving runestone is believed to be the Einangstein above Slidre in Valdres, Oppland, Norway, which dates from the latter half of the third century.

Resemblance of some runic letters to those in the North Italic alphabet suggests that the runes may have originated among those Germanic tribes living within, or at least close to, the Roman Empire, and subsequently spread northward into the Baltic region and beyond. The first complete runic alphabet, or futhark (so named for its first six letters, "th" being considered a single letter), appears on an early fifth-century runestone on the Swedish island of Gotland, and it contains twenty-four letters. This Elder Futhark, as it is usually called, was replaced by the beginning of the Viking Age (mid- to late eighth century) with the sixteen-letter Younger Futhark. In Anglo-Saxon England, on the other hand, the Old English Futhark was expanded to thirty-three letters.

On objects such as swords, spears, and axes, runes often spelled out the name of the maker, the owner, or the weapon itself. On amulets that were worn about the neck or carried in a pouch, the runes were thought to bring good luck (especially in love) or to guard against various dangers. On runestones, most of which are free-standing with one or more dressed faces, inscriptions frequently commemorate the dead, but some recount the accomplishments of the living. A classic example of the latter appears on a runestone now standing in the University Park in downtown Uppsala, Sweden. It reads (in translation): "Vigmundr had this stone cut in memory of himself, the most skilled of men. God help the soul of the skipper, Vigmundr."

Some forty runic inscriptions have been discovered in North America, although none of them has as yet been considered authentic by most archaeologists or runologists. The most famous of these inscriptions appears on the Kensington Runestone, which can be seen at the Runestone Museum in Alexandria, Minnesota. The 200-pound stone was discovered embraced by the roots of a tree by a Swedish farmer in 1898. Wisconsin historian H. R. Holand translated the inscription, which tells of a joint Norwegian-Swedish expedition in 1362 (shortly after the Black Death decimated the population of Scandinavia) that ran afoul of local Native Americans and lost a third of its party. Whether this runestone is authentic or a deliberate hoax has long been a matter of controversy.

As mundane and secular as most of the runestone inscriptions appear to be, there is more to the letters themselves than meets the eye. The individual letters or runes (the name coming from a Germanic word often translated as "secret" or "mysterious") not only served as part of a functional alphabet but also were linked to pre-Christian magico-religious practices. In that context the runes symbolized key concepts in the Germanic world-view. This notion has been challenged by some academic scholars such as R. I. Page, but one has only to open the pages of the *Poetic Edda* and read from the "Havamal" to remove all doubt as to whether or not our ancestors considered the runes to have magical properties:

> "Runes you will find, readable staves—
> Powerful magic, mighty spells—
> Made by great powers,
> The wisdom of Odin."

In that poem, Odin not only describes in detail the painful sacrifice he made (Chapter Five) to gain the secret meanings and powers of the runes, but he goes on to enumerate the magical properties of eighteen of them—ranging from those giving protection against weapons or fire to those that calm the sea, heal the wounded, cause the dead to speak, and win a woman's heart. Unfortunately, Odin does not tell us which runes possess which properties. In some cases, however, the names the runes bear (which have survived in a few runic poems) provide some insight into the roles they may have played. Those names represent various natural, psychological, or mythological phenomena (see Table One), each of which serves as a powerful metaphorical symbol.

In addition to the protective properties attributed to the runes, our forebears believed that runes could be used to cast spells—thus altering circumstances for oneself or another person—or to foretell the future by casting runic lots. Runecasting is probably largely responsible for the resurgence of interest in runes during the past two decades. Numerous books have been published on the subject, but most of them are seriously flawed—in my opinion—because they attempt to integrate the runes with systems from other cultures or perspectives (e. g.: I Ching, kabbala, eco-feminism, Wicca, tarot, theosophy, pop psychology). Trying to force a square peg into a round hole rarely works to the benefit of either. The two books that have been the most successful at examining the symbolic value of the runes within their proper Germanic cultural and historical contexts are Edred Thorsson's *Futhark* and *Runelore*, both of which are highly recommended to anyone wishing to explore this fascinating subject in greater depth.

For those who find themselves drawn to the runes but reluctant to study them because of a dislike, or fear, of their magical associations, let me assure you that my wife and I have found them to serve as marvelous foci for visual imagery as part of a meditative ritual. Let me give you one example. If you are discouraged by encountering a seemingly insurmountable barrier across your life's path, try to focus on the I-rune ("ice") and visualize yourself possessing the painstakingly slow, but ultimately irresistible, force of a glacier (the most powerful form of ice we know). Doing so can lead to a sense of calmness, patience, and a restoration of your self-confidence. Other runes can speak to other situations.

Dragons of the North

The Nordic peoples have always been fascinated by dragons, perhaps more so than any other culture save the Chinese and Japanese. Dragons completely dominated the arts and literature of the ancient North insofar as mythic animals are concerned. Nowhere is this more apparent than on the runestones, many of which figure a dragon or serpent (the ancient Norse made little distinction between them, referring to both as an orm) encircling a cross or highly stylized World Tree (inside back cover), perhaps yet another symbolic representation of our ancestors' recognition of the dynamic balance existing between Order and Chaos.

Although some writers have assumed that the central figure on these runestones always represents a Christian cross—and some of them surely do—the fact that a number of these figures have "tree roots," and that the expanded portion of the figure comprises eight vanes radiating from a central ring (Ymir's eyebrows?), seems to argue at least as strongly that—in those cases—we are seeing a symbolic representation of Yggdrasil. It is even possible that some Christian artists of the time equated the Cross with the World Tree.

Jörmungand, the Midgard Serpent, is the most prominent named dragon in Norse mythology. Also important is Nidhögg, chief among those great reptiles that dwell in the Well of Creation and gnaw on a root of Yggdrasil.

A very different, but equally famous, dragon was Fafnir, whose fateful encounter with Sigurd was a highlight of the greatest heroic legend of the North—a story recounted in the *Volsunga Saga* and in Richard Wagner's classic opera cycle *The Ring of the Nibelungs*. Fafnir was once a man, but—thanks to the curse of a magic ring—he slew his father for a golden treasure, cheated his brother out of his share, and then magically transformed himself into a dragon so he could guard his precious hoard.

Fafnir's brother Regin became a blacksmith. When Sigurd, the young son of the fallen hero Sigmund, came to Regin for training, the smith saw his chance to get revenge on Fafnir. Regin reforged Sigmund's broken sword for Sigurd, and taught him how to become a great warrior. Together, Regin and Sigurd hunted down Fafnir, whom Sigurd killed with the sword—after some timely advice from Odin. As Sigurd roasted the dragon's heart for Regin, he burned a finger on the bloody flesh. Putting the injured finger in his mouth, Sigurd sucked on it to relieve the pain. When he did so, he inadvertently swallowed some of the dragon's blood and could immediately understand the language of the birds twittering in a nearby tree. They warned Sigurd that Regin planned to kill him for Fafnir's treasure, so Sigurd struck first and won the dragon's hoard—and with it Andvari's curse that whoever kept the Dwarf's ring for himself would die.

Notice that in this story the dragon's blood is a source of hidden knowledge, just as the runes are a source of hidden knowledge. Thus it seems more than coincidental that—on the runestones—the runes are artistically represented as being contained within the dragon's body. This connection strikes me as being one of the more powerful metaphors coming out of the Norse myths and legends.

On a bare rock face near Ramsund, Sweden, is inscribed a huge image of Sigurd slaying the dragon Fafnir, tasting the dragon's blood, and—having learned from the birds of Regin's evil intentions—cutting off the smith's head. This whole scene is encircled by the dragon, which bears the runic inscription along the length of its body. To see this runic figure firsthand is to be struck both by its size (it's nearly 15 feet across) and the meticulous attention to detail given to this work by the artist who produced it. Incidentally, the inscription honors the memory of the husband of the woman who commissioned its cutting; it says nothing whatsoever about the story that the figure portrays.

Aside from Jörmungand, Nidhögg, and Fafnir—each of whom the ancient Norse considered to be evil—dragons in general seem to have been viewed as powerful, untameable forces of nature that were neither good nor evil. In fact, by placing dragon heads on stave-church gables and ship's prows, the ancient Norse thought they could invoke the power of the dragon to ward off evil beings such as trolls. So convinced were the Vikings of this power that they were careful to remove the dragon's head when their ship approached their home coastline, so that they wouldn't frighten the nature spirits of their own land.

TABLE ONE:

The Elder Futhark, with Runic Meanings and Commentary

F   ᚠ   cattle (= mobile property), wealth
[Thorsson's interpretation of this rune as the source of cosmic fire (= Muspellheim's rune?) is appealing, but it seems to be purely intuitive.]

U   ᚢ   aurochs (Audhumla?), drizzle
[As Audhumla's rune, this would seem to be the rune of creation, of revealing the true nature of that which lies concealed.]

TH   ᚦ   giant
[Primal matter and emotions (dangerous if uncontrolled). Countered by Thor (according to Thorsson), but not explicitly his rune.]

A   ᚨ   Aesir god (= Odin)
[Rune of the seeker after knowledge and wisdom, both of the outer and inner worlds. This is Odin's rune.]

R   ᚱ   riding, wagon
[Rune of the journey (external/internal) and the means by which it is taken.]

K   ᚲ   torch

[Controlled fire to illuminate the dark and/or creatively alter the material/psychic world (e. g., the forge).]

G   ᚷ gift

[Rune of love/friendship between two persons. "A gift calls for a gift." ("Havamal," *Poetic Edda.*)]

W   ᚹ joy

[Ecstatic happiness; the numinous experience.]

H   ᚺ hail

[Thorsson's "rune mother" concept of ᚺ as the cosmic egg seems to be purely intuitive, but ᚻ (an alternate form) does combine ᛁ and ᚴ (fire, reversed) if Thorsson is correct that ᚴ represents cosmic fire.]

N   ᚾ need

[Rune to be used when help is desperately needed.]

I   ᛁ   ice

[Rune of patience, perseverance, and self-control. Niflheim's contribution to creation.]

J   ᛃ year, season, harvest

[Rune of fertility; annual cycle of birth, growth, and death (= cycle of the seasons).]

EI   ᛇ   yew tree

[Rune of Yggdrasil, which binds and supports the Nine Worlds. May also be the rune of Ull, god of the yew bow.]

P   ᛈ   dice cup

[Rune of chance, embracing the unpredictable. Fulfilling one's destiny by following one's *wyrd*. The rune of the Norns?]

Z   ᛉ   protection, elk (= moose)

[Rune to avert danger (especially psychic). In Norway, the moose is "king of the forest."]

S   ᛋ   sun

[With ᛦ this is a powerful symbol of growth. ⚡ = the sun wheel, the thunderbolt.]

T   ᛏ   Tyr

[Rune of courage and self-sacrifice. Victory rune. Thorsson calls it the law and justice rune.]

B   ᛒ   birch tree, birch twig, birch goddess

[The cycles of nature; of green, living things. Rune of the earth mother (Jörd?).]

E ᛗ horse (= Sleipnir)

[Transportation between the worlds of the psyche. The shaman's spirit helper. Thorsson calls it the rune of the *fylgja.*]

M ᛘ man

[Rune of humankind, generally; of the individuated self, specifically—according to Thorsson.]

L ᛚ water

[With ᛋ, this is a powerful symbol of growth. Thorsson equates ᛚ with the "primeval cosmic water from Niflheim." Jung considers water to represent the Unconscious; I see ᛚ as the healing, cleansing power of running water.]

NG ◇ Ing (= Frey)

[Rune of fertility: of crops, livestock, and humans. Thorsson suggests that ◇ represents the cosmic seed that breaks open to energize the growth seen in ᛋ.]

D ᛞ day, daylight

[Rune of dawn/twilight, of the transitions between light and dark. The rune of balance and enlightenment.]

O   ᛟ inherited land or possessions
[Rune of ancestral heritage in all aspects: material, genetic, and spiritual.]

CHAPTER TEN: To Ragnarök . . . and Beyond

Ragnarök, the Doom of the Gods

> "Brothers will battle to bloody end,
> And sisters' sons their kinsman slay;
> Woe is in the world, depravity abounds;
> An axe age, a sword age—shattered are shields—
> A wind age, a wolf age, ere the world dies;
> No mercy will one man show another."
> —"Voluspa," *Poetic Edda*

Prior to Balder's fatal encounter with the mistletoe dart, Odin had ridden to Hel Gate to summon up the spirit of a dead *volva*, or seeress, to interpret Balder's nightmares. Reluctantly the *volva* told Odin her vision of the Nine Worlds, from its creation to its end—her vision forms the content of the Eddic poem we know as "Voluspa." The ending of which she spoke is called Ragnarök, the Doom of the Gods.

The *volva* said that Ragnarök will be preceded by Fimbul Winter, three consecutive winters with no intervening summers. These unbearable living conditions will see a complete breakdown in human society. Then two giant wolves will swallow the sun and the moon, and Ragnarök will commence.

Three roosters will crow—one in Jötunheim to waken the giants, one in Asgard to waken the heroes in Valhalla, and one in Hel to waken the Dead. Heimdall will sound the Gjallarhorn to warn the gods of the giants' approach. The forces of Order and Chaos shall meet on Vigrid Plain, and the Final Battle will begin.

Aside from the general slaughter, there will be a series of individual combats. Surt, Lord of the Fire Giants, will slay Frey, who shall have only a deer's antler to defend himself, his magic sword having been given up as Gerd's bride-price. Fenris Wolf will swallow Odin, only to be slain in turn by All-Father's son Vidar, who will break the wolf's neck. On one foot, Vidar will wear a special boot—its sole made thick by the accumulated leather scraps that bootmakers are supposed to discard for just this occasion. Heimdall and Loki will kill each other, as will Tyr and the Hel Hound, Garm. Thor will finally succeed in smashing the Midgard Serpent, but then will die himself, overcome by Jörmungand's venom.

After the slaughter has abated, Surt will wield his flaming sword and set the Nine Worlds ablaze. Eventually, the ravaged earth will sink into the sea. It will be the end of the Age.

Time will pass, and the earth will re-emerge from the sea, green and fair once more. Of the elder gods, only Hoenir will have survived—and taken custody of the runes[30]. Odin's sons Vali and Vidar will also survive, as will Thor's sons Magni and Modi, who will inherit their father's magic hammer, Mjöllnir. And, perhaps most marvelous of all, Balder and Höd shall return from Hel's domain. Moreover, two humans—Lif (Life) and Lifthrasir (Life-giving)—will emerge from their shelter in the remains of Yggdrasil to begin the human race anew. It will be the start of the New Age.

Lindow (in his 1997 paper "Murder and vengeance among the gods: Balder in Scandinavian mythology," *FF Communications* 262) emphasizes that the reconciliation of Balder (the victim), Höd (the killer, however inadvertent), and Vali (the avenger) in the New Asgard clearly means that the traditional demands of blood revenge will have been put aside. Thus the fires of Ragnarök will not only end

end the Aesir-jötnar feud (by eliminating the giants and the most belligerent of the gods), but also will purge all of the flaws in the cosmos.

Lindow's optimistic interpretation, however appealing, leaves unresolved the question of who will come forth to be the wives of the New Age Aesir—an unnamed daughter of Sol is the only female deity said to survive Ragnarök. It also assumes that Mjöllnir will be used only for ritual purposes. Finally, the presence of Nidhögg, the black dragon of Niflheim, in the closing stanza of "Voluspa" (*Poetic Edda*) where he flies up from the Dark Fjell bearing corpses, is highly significant. Clunies Ross sees Nidhögg's flight as a recognition by the poet that mortality continues to be a part of the New Order. Not only do I agree with her, but I would further suggest that it signifies a restoration of the dynamic equilibrium between Order and Chaos, which was temporarily disrupted by the deaths of Thor and Jörmungand. The names of the respective champions may change, but the *ørlög* endures.

Has Ragnarök already taken place, and are we living in the New Age? Or is the Doom of the Gods yet to come? Only the *volva* knows for certain, and she isn't saying.

Beyond Ragnarök: Walking the Northern Path

If our ancestors believed that even the gods were doomed to lose in the end, how did they avoid giving in to hopelessness and despair? They did so by choosing to embrace the *drengskapur*, the ethic and attributes of the Nordic hero (Table Two, page 231), a choice available to every individual . . . not just to warriors. By striving for personal excellence, one need not defeat life's foes in a physical, secular sense in order to have a meaningful existence. As John Greenway (*The Golden Horns: Mythic Imagination and the Nordic Past*) has said, ". . . nobility lies not in the confident expectation of triumph but in the resisting of the latent tide of chaos . . . ." In fact, Tolkien has been cited (by Tom Shippey, 2000, *J. R. R. Tolkien: Author of the Century*) as saying that this heroic ethic was the great contribution to humanity of the old literature of the North.

It was not a philosophy of grim fatalism that our ancestors embraced (though some writers have claimed that it was). The Nordic hero cherished existence and knew how to enjoy life, but could also face death with a calm mind and a smile. No matter what happened, a hero could choose to behave with honor and try to embody the *drengskapur*. "It matters not if you win or lose, but how you play the game" could well be the modern paraphrase of an old Norse saying such as the following verse attributed to Odin:

"Cattle die, kindred die.
Every man is mortal.
But the good name will never fade
Of one who has lived honorably."
—"Havamal," *Poetic Edda*

Walking the Northern Path has connected me to my ancestors, led me to my soul-mate, expanded my understanding of the world around me, and helped me to develop a satisfying personal philosophy of life. May it do as much—and more—for you.

TABLE TWO: *Drengskapur*:
The Heroic Code of Viking Age Scandinavia

Sannferdighet ("truthfulness")—always be honest

Hjelpsomhet ("helpfulness")—aid those in need

Trofasthet ("loyalty")—be true to those who are true to you

Sjelestyrke ("fortitude")—hang in there when life gets tough

Tapperhet ("courage")—face your fears

Selvrespekt ("self-respect")—do nothing to harm your integrity or good name

Selvbestemmelse ("self-determination")—take charge of your own life

Selvstyre ("self-restraint")—control your behavior

Selvstendighet ("self-reliance")—don't ask others to do for you what you can do for yourself

AFTERWORD: Echoes of Odin—Mythic Survival and Revival

As an organized religion with priests and temples, Asatru (a name by which the worship of Norse deities is sometimes called) ceased to be a major factor in the spiritual life of Northern Europe by the twelfth century, although individual worship may well have continued on a small scale for some time thereafter. The latter part of the twentieth century saw a revival of Asatru in the Scandinavian countries, England, and America, but the number of worshippers in each country is very small.

Although the indigenous Nordic religion had largely disappeared by the Saga Age (ca. 1200-1400 A. D.), for several centuries thereafter the mythic symbols survived—but mostly as secondary elements in sagas (which continued to be popular in Iceland) and as fragments of Nordic folklore. The myths and their symbols re-emerged on the European literary scene with the re-publication of the two *Eddas* in Denmark in 1665. This event coincided with a rise in intense nationalism in the Nordic countries, which were attempting to establish their national identities as separate and distinct from the politically and intellectually more dominant nations to the south. It is not surprising that some leaders seized upon the Norse myths as reflecting a "Golden Age of the North," a time when their ancestors—often in the role of Vikings—ruled Northern Europe, had an impact on many other parts of the continent, and even extended their influence across the North Atlantic.

By the mid-eighteenth century, interest in the stories and symbols of the mythic past was intensified by the influence of the Romantic period on Nordic art and literature. Romanticism placed a higher value on the natural world and mysticism than on urbanism and sophistication, contrasting world views that are still with us today. Among the most influential Scandinavian Romantic writers during the first half of the nineteenth century were Grundtvig in Denmark, Geijer in Sweden, and Wergeland and Welhaven in Norway.

The revived interest in Norse mythology probably reached its peak during the latter half of the nineteenth century, but the abuse of the mythological symbols by totalitarian militants in Germany (especially Hitler and the Nazis) during the second quarter of the twentieth century caused any interest in the Norse myths and the runes to be viewed with suspicion in Scandinavia and America during this period and the early post-World War II years. However, the need to identify with the symbols of one's cultural heritage as a way of psychologically connecting with one's ancestral roots has re-surfaced very strongly in recent decades (e. g., the response in America to Alex Haley's television mini-series *Roots* by people of diverse ethnic backgrounds). This phenomenon not only validates our interest in Norse mythology, but promises that it will continue to be important for Nordic peoples and their American kinfolk for generations to come.

During the past century-and-a-half, the Mythic Revival has been expressed in many different ways: in names (of persons, places, ships, days of the week, schools, businesses, etc.); in customs (especially those associated with Yuletide and New Year's); in folklore (stories and sayings in America as well as Scandinavia); and in arts and crafts, literature, music[31] and other entertainment[32]. Many examples appear throughout this book, but certain others are discussed below.

The use of Odin and, especially, Thor (often in a compound form such as Thorbjörn, Thorstein, Thorvald, etc.) as personal names still occurs in Scandinavia and, less frequently, in Scandinavian America. When, in 1862, some Norwegian immigrants joined the Union Army to fight in the Civil War, they formed an all-Norwegian infantry regiment, the 15th Wisconsin, one company of which called themselves "Odin's Rifles."

A survey of the Oslo, Norway, and Stockholm, Sweden, telephone directories in 1998 revealed at least three dozen businesses and schools in Oslo (and twice that many in Stockholm) bearing the name of a figure from Norse mythology. Odin[33] was by far the most popular name in Stockholm; in Oslo, Balder was equally popular. In America, the Tyr swimwear company was named in honor of the courage and competitive spirit of the Norse war god, and the power and adventurous spirit of Thor inspired the logo of the makers of Thor motorcycling accessories.

An examination of street maps for present-day Oslo and Stockholm reveals more evidence of the influence of the Mythic Revival in Norway and Sweden. In 1896, Oslo authorities named the following streets (gate, pronounced "gata" = street): Odins gate, Valkyriegate, Tors gate, Balders gate, Vidars gate, and Åsaveien. In 1914, Iduns gate, Sigyns gate, and Frøyas gate were added. In Stockholm, the names were given in the following chronological order: 1885—Valhallavägen, Odengatan, Torsgatan, Frejagatan, Vanadisvägen; 1900—Idunagatan; 1906—Heimdalsgatan, Vidargatan; 1909—Baldersgatan, Bragevägen, Friggagatan, Tyrgatan; 1926—Völundsgatan.

Five days of the week are still named after Norse deities: Monday (*mandag* in Norwegian, Mani's day); Tuesday (*tirsdag*, Tyr's Day); Wednesday (*onsdag*, Odin's Day); Thursday (*torsdag*, Thor's Day); and Friday (*fredag*, Frigg's Day). This is one of the most pervasive ways in which Norse mythology impinges on our lives today, but most people are completely ignorant of the connection.

Finally, five of the moons of Saturn first discovered in 2000-2001 were given the names of Norse giants: Ymir, Suttung, Mundilfari, Skadi, and Thrym.

Many myth-related customs are associated with Yuletide. The name itself may have come from the Scandinavian words *hjul* ("wheel") and *tid* ("time" or "season"). Thus "Wheeltime" could refer to the passage of the Sun Wheel through the sky, and reflect the fact that the sun appears to be farthest from the northern lands in midwinter. It has been suggested that burning the Yule Log was intended originally to light the way for the Chariot of the Sun to return to the North.

At that time of year during the Viking Age, it was customary for a live boar to be led into the hall. There the assembled warriors would take turns placing their hands upon its back and making vows to Frey (for whom the boar was a sacred animal) about the great deeds they would accomplish in the year ahead. Then the boar would be killed, cooked, and eaten. From these acts may come the origin of New Year's resolutions and the frequent association of pork with Yuletide feasts.

The origin of the Christmas Tree apparently is not as ancient as the Norse myths, but some sources (Carla Wenckebach's *A Christmas Book*) tell us that during the Romantic period, the decorated fir tree was intended to represent Yggdrasil, the World Tree. The fact that the ornaments from that era included sugar or papier-maché deer, goats, eagles, cats, horses, squirrels, boars, ravens, and wolves suggests that this interpretation may be correct.

That symbols from myth and folklore are still deeply embedded in the Nordic consciousness is surely reflected in a 1975 survey in Iceland conducted by the university in Reykjavik. The survey revealed, among other things, that 55% of those questioned believed that the literal existence of elves and huldrefolk (figures from folklore that seem to be intermediate between elves and trolls) is "at least plausible." Before shrugging off this poll's results as simply being due to ignorant superstition, it would be wise to remember that Iceland has the highest literacy rate of any nation in the world.

Norwegians also are psychologically drawn to these symbols. If you examine a Norwegian dictionary, you will find 38 compound words containing "troll" as either a prefix or suffix; by comparison, English has only 19 compound words containing "witch."

In King Harald's New Year's address to the Norwegian people in 1998, he said the following: " . . . let us not be a nation of sad faces. Most of us have little reason to be depressed. It is important to get back the zest for life and take up the fight against the trolls as Askeladden does. Our problems can have three or nine heads, but with courage and an indomitable spirit we can, as our Norwegian fairy tale character, win many a personal victory." What wonderful evidence that the traits and spirit of the *drengskapur* are still alive and well in the Norwegian psyche—and where in the West but in Scandinavia could a head-of-state be able to make a serious allusion to folklore figures and expect that his audience would both understand what he was talking about and not think him silly for doing so? To King Harald and his people we owe a debt of gratitude for helping to keep the Northern Path cleared of underbrush and open for us to follow.

END NOTES

1. Details of the *idrottir* are contained in my 1984 book, *Viking Lore: Viking Age Activities for Today's Young People,* which is available from Sons of Norway Heritage Programs, 1455 West Lake Street, Minneapolis, MN 55408.

2. "Beyond Odin," Sept. 1992; "The Nine Worlds," Oct. 1992; "Fate's victim or hero?" Nov. 1992; "The truth about trolls," Oct. 1994; "The riddle of the runes," May 1995.

3. "Ancient Nordic spirituality: a quest for wisdom and balance," Fall 1996.

4. This is according to the "Lay of Vafthrudnir," *Poetic Edda.* Trolls are more likely than giants to have multiple heads, although the distinction between the two kindred is often blurred in the myths.

5. We are not told the motive for Creation's first act of violence, save that Odin declared Ymir and all of his descendants to be evil. How a giant who did nothing but sleep could be evil is never explained, nor is there any acknowledgment that the gods themselves are descendants of Ymir on the maternal side. Confusing and unsettling as such inconsistencies are to modern readers, logic and consistency are not characteristic of mythological stories generally.

6. Since the sky grows light before the sun appears, apparently our ancestors didn't see a cause-and-effect relationship between the two. Or perhaps they did . . . and just thought this made a better story!

7. References to her brood as being kin to Fenris, the most famous wolf in Norse mythology, suggest that the Hag may be none other than Angrboda herself, Loki's grim consort.

8. The *Poetic Edda* tells us that Odin was accompanied by Hoenir and Lodur (= Loki?) rather than by his brothers, Vili and Ve. In any

event, the creation of Humankind from trees should be an appealing metaphor to those—such as I—who have a strong emotional tie to all things green and growing.

9. I realize that neither snakes nor dragons have teeth suitable for gnawing wood (or anything else). This is another instance where we simply have to accept the poetic license of myth.

10. Clunies Ross wonders why the arrival of three giant maidens in Asgard soon after that land was established by the Aesir should have been disruptive. Hollander, in his translation of the *Poetic Edda*, flatly states that those maidens were, in fact, the Norns. If he is correct, then the onset of the Norns' weaving the Tapestry of Fate would have introduced a factor that the gods could neither order nor control, and to which they themselves would be subject.

11. Reference to "the Well" simply follows the terminology used by Bauschatz. Clearly, the water in Hvergelmir and Mimir's Well also comes from Yggdrasil—and returns to the Tree by way of its roots. This interrelationship among all three Wells cannot be overstressed.

12. Andy Orchard, *Dictionary of Norse Myth and Legend*, lists 156 of those names in an appendix.

13. Clunies Ross argues that Heimdall's father was more likely Njörd, but the *Prose Edda* clearly lists Heimdall as a son of Odin.

14. This seeming contradiction might be resolved if Tyr actually were Odin's son by Hymir's wife, but was subsequently raised by his mother in Hymir's hall with the giant treating Tyr as if he were his own son. This is mere speculation on my part, and it should be noted that, despite his many sexual liaisons, Odin apparently never became involved with a married woman—in fact, he warns against such behavior in the "Havamal" (*Poetic Edda*). In any event, when Tyr became an adult, he moved to Asgard.

15. The *Prose Edda* tells us that half of the fallen warriors will dwell in Folkvang with the goddess Freyja. We do not know if they, too, will serve in Odin's army, or if they have some other role to play.

16. It is not unusual in matrilineal and matrilocal societies for a boy's maternal uncle—rather than his father—to take responsibility for training the boy to assume his role as a man. But the other views we are afforded of giant society in the myths and legends seem to indicate that it is as patrilineal and patrilocal as that of the Aesir.

17. Some authors (e. g., Ralph Metzner, *The Well of Remembrance*) have suggested that the reconciliation between two tribes of gods—which was initiated by the Vanir despite their being the offended party and having the upper hand when the truce was declared—is one of the most important lessons the Norse myths have to offer.

18. Trance induction may be brought about by auto-suggestion, or be assisted by drumming (e. g., among the Saami) or by a drug such as that contained in the fly-agaric mushroom, which is often found near birch trees. Eating this mushroom produces a feeling of increased strength and agility, followed by hallucinations (e. g., objects seem larger), and finally a loss of awareness of your surroundings.

19. The numerous descriptions in the myths of shape-changing by Odin and others may well have been attempts to literalize the role of spirit helpers by commentators who did not fully understand the shamanic paradigm. Snorri, however, clearly did understand, for in the "Ynglinga Saga" (*Heimskringla*) he said that Odin could, while in a trance, send his spirit to visit far-off places in the form of a beast, bird, fish, or orm (snake or dragon).

20. Metzner calls our attention to the term "raven's bread" as being a widespread ancient name for the fly-agaric mushroom, an

association with the possible shamanic spirit-helper role of Hugin and Munin that can hardly be coincidental. Note should also be made of the two wolves, Freki and Geri, that are said to sit by Odin's throne in Asgard. These wolves may also be his *fylgjur*, but none of the stories recounts them doing anything other than eating from Odin's plate while he consumes only wine. And, of course, his eight-legged horse, Sleipnir, may also be considered a spirit helper—a Saami shaman sometimes referred to his drum, which helped conduct him to the spirit world, as his "horse."

21. Clunies Ross has pointed out that Balder's funeral, which drew together representatives of all beings in a common sorrow, would have been an opportunity for a reconciliation between the gods and giants. But Thor spoiled the occasion—and violated the neutrality of a sacred setting—by threatening to kill Hyrrokin (a giantess invited by the gods to come and help them launch Balder's funeral ship) and, then, by actually killing Lit, a Dwarf who got underfoot.

22. Lindow (in his 1997 article "Murder and vengeance among the gods: Balder in Scandinavian mythology," *FF Communications* 262) reminds us that kin-slaying, even when "justified" by motives of vengeance, was still a violation of the Norse social order. He sees the Balder myth as representing the doomed nature of the Aesir.

23. Their mother was Njörd's sister (Nerthus?), incest being an accepted practice among the Vanir. Such behavior was forbidden among the Aesir.

24. Snorri says they are "fairer than the sun to look upon," and the Old Norse expression *frið sem alfkona* ("fair as an Elf-woman") reflects the apex of feminine loveliness.

25. The Viking-Age Norse believed that the Lapps (Saami) had magical powers: that their shamans could travel out-of-body, control

the weather, and prophesy by using a magic drum. The Saami fertility god, Vaeralden-olmai ("man of the world"), corresponds to Frey, who was given Alfheim as a tooth-gift in Norse mythology and thus, presumably, was the patron deity of the Light Elves thereafter. And, most specifically, in "Völundarkvida" (*Poetic Edda*), it is clearly stated that Völund is a son of a Lapp king, and there are repeated references to his being an Elf lord.

26. The sun is referred to as "Dvalin's Doom," and a nickname for the Dwarf Dvalin is Solblindi ("sun-blinded"). Incidentally, certain of the lesser Norns are referred to by the kenning "daughters of Dvalin," which should put to rest the suggestion by several prominent mythologists that female Dwarves don't exist!

27. The Old English equivalent is ettins, the Anglo-Saxon is ents. The latter term is the one that J. R. R. Tolkien applied to Treebeard and his kin in *The Lord of the Rings*.

28. My grandmother told me of being warned in 1890 by her Norwegian-born grandmother: "Don't go out after dark or the four-heads will get you!" Clearly the trolls succeeded in coming over to America with the immigrants.

29. Loki is said to be the son of the giant Farbauti and his wife, Laufey (a giantess? a goddess?). Often referred to as Loki Laufeyjarson, he seems to be unique in the ancient Norse world in being named after his mother rather than his father. However, because of Loki's close association with fire, the fact that the chief Fire Giant Surt's wife, Sinmara, keeps Loki's sword under lock-and-key for him ("Svipdagsmal," *Poetic Edda*), and a statement that Loki will steer the ship carrying the forces of Muspellheim to the Final Battle at Ragnarök ("Voluspa," *Poetic Edda*), I have long wondered

if Loki might not actually be a Fire Giant—perhaps the son of Surt and Sinmara—and that he had been fostered to Laufey and Farbauti. 30. We are told ("Vafthrudnismal," *Poetic Edda*) that Njörd will return to Vanaheim at Ragnarök, but it isn't clear if this means he will survive the final conflagration or merely that he will go home to die with his kinfolk. Freyja's fate is never mentioned in the myths. Several writers have quoted Snorri—out of context—as saying that "Freya alone remained of the gods," but that statement appears only in the "Ynglinga Saga" section of his *Heimskringla*, which treats the gods as glorified humans who died natural deaths, and it makes no mention of Ragnarök or its survivors.

31. From its first performance in 1876, Richard Wagner's unique and powerful four-part operatic interpretation of the story of the Ring of the Nibelungs has remained the most vivid and memorable use of Norse mythic material on stage. A contemporary American rock-opera *The Rhymer and the Ravens*, based on Jodie Forrest's novel of the same name, makes extensive and imaginative use of both Norse and Celtic mythology. The Swedish rock-group Garmarna features Garm, the Hound of Hel, as its logo, and Led Zeppelin has referred to Norse myths in some of its lyrics, to mention just a few examples.

32. Nordic Fest, which is held in July in Decorah, Iowa, has a parade that often features giant puppets representing various characters from the Norse myths, and the bonfire that precedes the closing fireworks is called Balder's Fire in memory of Balder's funeral pyre. Ullr Fest, held in Breckenridge, Colorado, in January, honors Ull, the Norse god of winter.

Two Scandinavian theme parks have recently featured myth-based attractions: Valhalla Castle at Tivoli Gardens in Copenhagen, Denmark; and a Viking voyage inside a mountain at Vikinglandet, just south of Oslo, Norway. Passengers on the "voyage" hear part of the volva's prophecy (from the poem "Voluspa"), experience their ship being attacked by a Midgard Serpent of truly frightening proportions, and see the roots of the World Tree—a very impressive and effective use of mythology in an amusement park setting. And, in America, the Norwegian pavilion at Epcot Center in Florida features a boat ride in which visitors enter Norway by sailing through the "eye of Odin" into the Maelstrom, the giant whirlpool famed in legend and literature.

33. Different Germanic languages often have different spellings for the names of the Norse gods. Some of the alternate spellings include: Odin, Oden, Woden, Wotan; Thor, Tor, Thunor, Donar; Frigg, Frigga, Fricka, Frija; Frey, Frø; Freyja, Freia, Freja, Frøya; Loki, Loke.

NORSE MYTHS & RUNELORE: A Selected Bibliography

Mythology:

Allan, Tony. *Vikings: The Battle at the End of Time.* London: Duncan Baird, 2002.

Barrett, Clive. *The Viking Gods: Pagan Myths of Nordic Peoples.* Wellingsborough, England: Aquarian Press, 1989.

Bauschatz, Paul C. *The Well and the Tree: World and Time in Early Germanic Culture.* Amherst: University of Massachusetts Press, 1982.

Branston, Brian. *Gods of the North.* New York: Thames and Hudson, 1955.

——————. *Gods & Heroes from Viking Mythology.* Beccles, England: Peter Lowe, 1978.

Brodeur, Arthur G., trans. *The Prose Edda* by Snorri Sturluson. New York: American-Scandinavian Foundation, 1916.

Clunies Ross, Margaret. *The Myths,* Vol I of *Prolonged Echoes: Old Norse Myths in Medieval Northern Society.* Denmark: Odense University Press, 1994.

Cotterell, Arthur. *Norse Mythology: The Myths and Legends of the Nordic Gods.* New York: Lorenz Books, 2000.

Crossley-Holland, Kevin. *The Norse Myths.* New York, Pantheon Books, 1980.

Daly, Kathleen N. *Norse Mythology A to Z: A Young Reader's Companion.* New York: Facts on File, Inc., 1991.

D'Aulaire, Ingri and Edgar. *Norse Gods and Giants.* Garden City, NY: Doubleday & Co., Inc., 1967.

DuBois, Thomas A. *Nordic Religions in the Viking Age.* Philadelphia: University of PA Press, 1999.

Dumézil, Georges. *Gods of the Ancient Northmen.* Berkeley: University of California Press, 1973.

Ellis Davidson, H. R. 1964. *Gods and Myths of Northern Europe.* Baltimore: Penguin Books, 1964.

——————————. 1969. *Scandinavian Mythology.* New York: Paul Hamlyn, 1969.

——————————. *Myths and Symbols in Pagan Europe: Early Scandinavian and Celtic Religions.* Syracuse: Syracuse Univ. Press, 1988.

——————————. *The Lost Beliefs of Northern Europe.* London: Routledge, 1993.

Evans, Cheryl, and Anne Millard. *Usborne Illustrated Guide to Norse Myths and Legends.* Tulsa: EDC Publ., 1987.

Faulkes, Anthony, trans. *Edda.* By Snorri Sturluson. London: Everyman Library, J. M. Dent, 1987.

Grant, John. *An Introduction to Norse Mythology.* Seacaucus, NJ: Chartwell Books, Inc., 1990.

Green, Roger L. *Myths of the Norsemen.* Baltimore, MD: Penguin Books, 1960.

Greenway, John L. *The Golden Horns: Mythic Imagination and the Nordic Past.* Athens, GA: University of Georgia Press, 1977.

Guerber, H. A. *Myths of the Norsemen from the Eddas and Sagas.* 1909; rpt. New York: Dover Publications, 1992.

Hollander, Lee M., trans. *The Poetic Edda.* 2nd Ed. Austin: University of Texas Press, 1986.

King, Cynthia. *In the Morning of Time: The Story of the Norse God Balder.* New York: Four Winds Press, 1970.

Laing, Samuel, trans. *Sagas of the Norse Kings.* Part Two of *Heimskringla.* By Snorri Sturluson. 1930; revised ed. Dutton, New York: Everyman's Library, 1961.

Lindow, John. *Myths & Legends of the Vikings.* Santa Barbara, CA: Bellerophon Books, 1979.

——————————. *Norse Mythology: A Guide to the Gods, Heroes, Rituals, and Beliefs.* New York: Oxford University Press, 2001.

MacCulloch, J. A. 2nd Ed. *The Celtic and Scandinavian Religions.* London: Constable & Co. Ltd., 1993.

Metzner, Ralph. *The Well of Remembrance: Rediscovering the Earth Wisdom Myths of Northern Europe.* Boston, MA: Shambhala Publications, 1994.

Orchard, Andy. *Dictionary of Norse Myth and Legend.* London: Cassell, 1997.

Page, R. I. *Norse Myths.* Austin: University of Texas Press, 1990.

Picard, Barbara L. *Tales of the Norse Gods and Heroes.* Oxford, England: Oxford University Press, 1953.

Roberts, Morgan J. *Norse Gods and Heroes.* New York: Metro Books, Friedman/Fairfax Publishers, 1995.

Rossman, Douglas ("Dag"). *Ice and Fire: Tales from Norse Mythology.* Minneapolis, MN: Skandisk, Inc., [audiocassette], 1992.

——————————. *Hammer and Mistletoe: Tales from Norse Mythology.* Minneapolis, MN: Skandisk, Inc., [audiocassette], 1993.

——————————. *Troll Tales.* Minneapolis, MN: Skandisk, Inc., [audiocassette], 1994.

——————————. *The Ring of Doom.* Minneapolis, MN: Skandisk, Inc., [audiocassette], 1996.

—————————. *The Nine Worlds: A Dictionary of Norse Mythology.* 2nd Ed. Bloomington, MN: Skandisk, Inc., 2000.

—————————. *Theft of the Sun, and Other New Norse Myths.* Bloomington, MN: Skandisk, Inc., 2001.

—————————, and Sharon C. Rossman. *Valhalla in America: Norse Myths in Wood at Rock Island State Park, Wisconsin.* Washington Island, WI: Jackson Harbor Press, 1999.

Simek, Rudolf. *Dictionary of Northern Mythology.* Cambridge, England: D. S. Brewer, 1953.

Sorensen, Villy. *The Downfall of the Gods.* Lincoln, NE: University of Nebraska Press, 1989.

Taylor, Paul B., and W. H. Auden, trans. *The Elder Edda: A Selection.* New York: Vintage Books, 1970.

Terry, Patricia, trans. *Poems of the Elder Edda.* Philadelphia, PA: University of Pennsylvania Press, 1990.

Titchnell, Elsa-Brita. *The Masks of Odin: Wisdom of the Ancient Norse.* Pasadena, CA: Theosophical University Press, 1995.

Young, Jean I., trans. *The Prose Edda of Snorri Sturluson: Tales from Norse Mythology.* By Snorri Sturluson. Berkeley, CA: University of California Press, 1954.

Runes and Runelore

Aswynn, Freya. *Leaves of Yggdrasil.* St. Paul, MN: Llewellyn Publications, 1990.

Conway, D. J. *Norse Magic.* St. Paul, MN: Llewellyn Publications, 1990.

Elliott, Ralph. *Runes, an Introduction.* Manchester, England: Manchester University Press, 1959.

Flowers, Stephen E(dred). *Runes and Magic: Magical Formulaic Elements in the Older Runic Tradition.* American University Studies Series 1, Vol. 53. New York: Peter Lang Publishing, Inc., 1986.

Gitlin-Emmer, Susan. *Lady of the Northern Light: A Feminist Guide to the Runes.* Freedom, CA: The Crossing Press, 1993.

Jansson, S. B. F. *The Runes of Sweden.* New York: Bedminster Press, 1962.

Jónasson, Björn. *A Little Book About the Runes.* Reykjavik, Iceland: GUDRUN [includes the Icelandic rune poem], 2001.

Moltke, E. *Runes and their Origin, Denmark and Elsewhere.* Copenhagen: National Museum of Denmark, 1985.

Page, R. I. *Runes.* Berkeley: University of California Press, 1987.

Paul, Jim, transl. *The Rune Poem: Wisdom's Fulfillment, Prophecy's Reach.* San Francisco: Chronicle Books [includes the Anglo-Saxon rune poem], 1996.

Thorsson, Edred. *Futhark: A Handbook of Rune Magic.* York Beach, ME: Samuel Weiser, Inc., 1984.

——————. *Runelore: A Handbook of Esoteric Runology.* York Beach, ME: Samuel Weiser, Inc., 1987.

——————. *At the Well of Wyrd: A Handbook of Runic Divination.* York Beach, ME: Samuel Weiser, Inc., 1988.

——————. *Northern Magic: Mysteries of the Norse, Germans & English.* St. Paul, MN: Llewellyn Publications, 1992.

Tyson, Donald. *Rune Magic.* St. Paul, MN: Llewellyn Publications, 1988.